GUNSTOCKS AND DOVETAILS

Thomas Hudson

CHIVERS LARGE PRINT
BATH

British Library Cataloguing in Publication Data available

This Large Print edition published by Chivers Press, Bath, 2001.

Published by arrangement with Tabb House.

U.K. Hardcover ISBN 0 7540 4614 1
U.K. Softcover   ISBN 0 7540 4615 X

Printed and bound in Great Britain by
Bookcraft, Midsomer Norton, Somerset

Set into stone their names carved crudely,
No one passing could help but see
Thomas Eden, William Bewdley,
James Llewellyn, and young Ted Lea.

Nothing is altered; rooks still quarrel
High in the elms over Bewdley's loft;
Still the meadows are plagued with sorrel,
Still the clover springs green and soft.

Evening passes with gentle fingers,
Sunshine fills in the sycamore tree,
And under the leaves the moth light lingers—
But William Bewdley's not there to see.

Here where life runs lustily, crudely,
This were heartbreak, to stand and see
Snatched for ever to silence—Bewdley,
Eden, Llewellyn, and young Ted Lea.

Katherine McIntosh

*from the Frank Palmer Cook papers, published
in* The Countryside at War, 1914–1918, *by
Caroline Dakers, Constable & Co Ltd, 1987*

PROLOGUE

When I left Hardwick's wheelwright's workshop at Nether Oldston to enlist in the army, I was entered for the Royal Engineers, but such were the methods of the army that I found myself making up a number for the Royal Army Medical Corps. During my first few days I had been lined up with a number of others, all for the REs, to be asked by a sergeant if anyone had ever pushed a wheelchair.

'Yes,' I said without thinking.

'Right, fall out and give me your name and number, then report to the Orderly Room straight away,' he ordered. When I objected I was told 'Stop complaining, soldier. If your boots aren't cleaner than that next time I see you, you'll be on a charge!'

It was useless to reason that my experience as a wheelwright might be more use to the engineers than my ignorance of even putting on a bandage. I learnt to keep my mouth shut from then on but I was transferred to the RAMC there and then, to be trained as a medical orderly-cum-ambulance driver-cum-stretcher bearer.

Before leaving Hardwick's my world had not extended more than twenty-five miles in any direction but within six weeks of joining up

1

I had crossed the English Channel to join a field hospital at Amiens. Six months later I was promoted to Lance Corporal and posted up the line to join a Regimental Aid Post with a battalion somewhere near Auchonvillers, and plunged into the bitter and bloody anguish of the Somme.

I cannot bring myself to write in detail of the sickening, heart-rending scenes that I was involved in during those months but in recounting my later years as a wheelwright and carpenter I cannot leave out some mention of that time. Although for me it lasted no more than two and a half years, it burned into my consciousness a searing grotesque awareness of what man was capable of doing to man, while I was still striving to live with some degree of normality among my comrades, and also with those at home when an unsteadying period of leave at last came round.

In those months I grew old. The green of the grass had faded. The mud of Flanders, the dread of the Somme had soiled my five senses. The song of the thrush, the trill of the blackbird, which had heralded hope and promise at dawn and evening in my blissful youth at home and at Nether Oldston, I had now heard in the deadly ravages of France. I had seen the wild flowers, celandine, primrose and bluebell, crushed and crumpled under the rotting corpses of comrades, and blue sky and gentle sunsets had been a backdrop to the blasphemy. The reassurance of the everyday tranquillity, the ordinary country life that I had grown up with had been marred for ever. Never again could I experience the innocence of youth.

What was it that old Ben James had said before I left?—'It'll do in six months to you what this 'ere village won't do in sixty years'; and it had.

CHAPTER ONE

Crash!—One evening about a year after arriving in France, I was asleep on the wooden chair in our field dressing post and was woken by the timber prop that held up one side of the trench doorway as it collapsed onto the stretcher unit. I could still hear the continuous rattle of gunfire and explosions, although muffled by the earth and sandbags that had fallen around me. Within minutes a second shell landed directly in the collapsed doorway and but for the landslide as a result of the first nearby shell, I should surely have been blown to pieces. Instead, I became entombed in the small space where the chair and stretcher unit were almost buried. Now all was silent as the earth settled around me. After a few seconds a timber frame near me creaked eerily from the weight of earth on it and with a final squawk

3

collapsed, to allow more earth and stones to trickle slowly at first but then come down with a frightening rush. I caught a flash of daylight from somewhere above then, like a mine shaft being filled in, it was blotted out, leaving me engulfed with only one arm able to move in the damp blackness. I felt panic. A thousand thoughts went through my mind in the same second. I think I yelled 'Stop it!'—more to myself in my rising fear than as an involuntary command to my attackers.

In the pitch darkness I could see nothing. All was silent. There was nothing I could do to estimate how long I would be able to go on breathing. As my circulation was restricted I quickly became numb with the cold and pressure. I cannot recall any of my thoughts during those minutes except one: I saw Hardwick's old carthorse, Magnolia, rubbing her backside on the old barn at home. There she stood, moving gently as she had done when I watched her from the gateway one evening when I had returned disconcerted from Sunday tea with Maisie Hawtin. She was the woodman's pretty daughter who lived near the wheelwright's shop where I worked. For as long as I took to lose consciousness I remembered the ecstasy in Magnolia's eyes in the evening light, while the old barn creaked regularly in protest as her great rounded rump abused it.

How long I remained unconscious I do not

4

know but my next sensation was of being bundled onto a stretcher and taken over the shell-cratered terrain to the Advanced Dressing Station.

Here sal-volatile was dabbed upon me and a sergeant, whom I had met previously during my few months' work in the Stationary Hospital, said 'You'll be all right, lad. There's some strong tea in that pot; pour me one and one for yourself. Sit and drink it, then come and help me with some of these men.'

The dressing station was simply an extension of the Aid Post where wounded men were brought for first aid and basic treatment. The medical officer in charge decided who could be returned to the battle and which cases should be sent back down the lines to the Main Dressing Station, or perhaps to the Casualty Clearing Station and then on to the Stationary Hospital. He also organised the burial of those whose wounds allowed no further movement in this world. Treatment there in those dug-out earth holes, damp, cold, infested with insects and running with rats, was primitive in the extreme. That anyone could survive a scratched finger in such conditions was a miracle of the human will to live, but we continued with our shuffling round with stretchers, bandaging and applying splints, bathing wounds in not-always-clean water but well laced with strong carbolic disinfectant, and administering morphine. From the field units the only way back for a wounded man to where a horse-drawn or motor-driven ambulance might be found was by stretcher over the terrain created by the tumultuous heavings of incessant bombardment. It was, nevertheless, of vital importance to keep the post as clear as possible, so the dispatch of casualties by one means or another was imperative.

This became very difficult when the wounded were brought in great numbers during a big push or raid. Then, after the firing had subsided the stretcher parties would go out and try to bring in those lying across the wastes of no-man's-land.

Captain Jackson was the medical officer in charge of the aid post that had been shelled. He was also in charge of the station to which I had been brought and the main dressing station, which was in the remains of a small farmhouse half a mile further back.

'Send him back for a bath and change of clothes, Sergeant,' he said, regarding my earth-stained battledress.

Two rooms still stood complete in the partly demolished farmhouse, although they were dark because the broken windows had been boarded over with old doors taken from a wood shed, and they were not dry because in heavy rain water soaked through the ceilings, the roof having gone completely.

When the captain had a break for tea he

would also drink lime juice, while reading all sorts of books and smoking a pipe. It was in these periods that he organised the acquisition of some heavy tarpaulins, which we managed to get over the top of the roof and tied down securely.

Men were brought in continuously, not only with physical wounds but suffering from exhaustion, mentally and spiritually. After a couple of days with clean dry socks and clothing, hot baths in old barrels and thick bread and jam, they returned to the firing lines. These 'extras' were obtained by the captain who wrote home asking for such things, including primus stoves by the dozen, and which folk at home sent out in response.

The station was manned mainly by conscientious objectors who were, however, prepared to help the maimed, and for them the heating of water and the washing of clothes was a never ending process.

Soon after being buried alive I was promoted to Corporal.

The doctor had said he would recommend me for a few days' rest if things quietened down a little but at this stage a new 'big push' started, our aid post became swamped with wounded and my chances of any rest back down the line disappeared.

'Bring two other stretcher bearers, Corporal, and we'll go and look for survivors,' the Doctor would say when darkness fell after a day's fighting and there were wounded men lying out in no-man's-land.

He was a brave man who simply ignored the danger of snipers and mines.

His father was a doctor and when war was declared he himself had recently qualified. Leaving his new appointment in a London hospital, he had volunteered for the RAMC. A devout Christian, in the absence of a Padre on Sunday, whenever possible he conducted a church service in the dressing station, using the prayer book which he always carried in his pocket and playing a mouth organ for hymn singing.

One evening he told me to take a stretcher party out while he took another. It had been raining most of the day; the barren land between the lines was a quagmire and when we crawled over the top of the front trench it had begun raining again. There was no moon but every so often an exploding shell or grenade would light up the landscape. The two men with me slid forward towards a crater where a voice was calling and we set about carrying another man back to safety. After a number of wounded had been brought in we discovered that the other party had not returned.

By this time we were wet with mud and rain and almost exhausted, but the three men we had brought in had been taken back to the aid post by other stretcher bearers, so we set out to look for the missing party.

We came across the doctor lying in a dark pool in a crater. He and his companions had hit a mine and the two other men had been blown to pieces. The doctor had lost a leg and part of his hip; he was unconscious and bleeding badly. We plugged the bleeding as best we could then slowly between shadows, for the rain had stopped and a moon was appearing between clouds, got him back to our trenches. I gave him morphine but feared he would be dead before we reached the aid post.

The sergeant took one look at him and told us to put him in an ambulance. 'Go with him, Abey. He's done for but you had better go,' he said.

I climbed in and sat beside him. I pulled my socks off and wiped my feet dry on a blanket. I could feel the mud congealing behind my knees and shivered inside my wet clothing. We swayed along over the rough road in the dark. There was no light. I tried to hear if he was breathing but the noise of the vehicle prevented it.

'Corporal,' he suddenly said, almost inaudibly.

'Yes sir?' I replied. There was a long pause and I held my ear close to him.

'Abey,' he said.

'I can hear you, Sir,' I said.

'My pocket.'

'Yes, Sir.'

'Prayer book,' he said.

9

I knew he kept it in one of his top pockets and felt for it. I unbuttoned the flap and took it out. 'It's here, Sir.'

'Send it to my father. Letters—my case,' he said.

'Yes, Sir. I'll do that.'

He said no more, and was dead by the time we arrived at the base hospital half an hour later.

Back at the aid post I found his small leather attaché case. As I had learned from months of handling what previously I could not have imagined doing, I opened the case. Inside it I found letters addressed to his father, Peter Jackson, and Miss Emily Ringwood, to whom he was engaged to be married. He had written them for the purpose of just this eventuality. The few personal belongings, comb, soap, writing materials, cough sweets, I left in the case and sent back down the line to be returned to his family. I wrapped the prayer book up with the two letters and, taking the address from the letter to his father, sent them with the postal collection.

Four weeks later I went with five others a few miles back to the casualty clearing station for a break from the front line post. Another friend, Dan Ayris, who had managed to survive with me so far, was one of the five.

'Break could be a good description of what we'll get there!' he remarked wryly. 'I was there for three months before and sleep is

10

unheard of.'

Nevertheless, it was slightly more civilised than the aid post and it was possible to spend short spells in the town of Albert during lulls in the fighting.

The whole of our existence was a strange one, especially for those involved in the front line area. The real and the unreal were so intricately interwoven that one's mind was subjected to severe strain. I had then had no home leave, and was not to get any until six months before the end of the war. Although this was a long time without leaving France, I found the experience of returning to the lines even after only seven short days too painful. In a way it was reassuring to find the old places and folk little changed, but the two scenes were incompatible and I found the readjustment too great. It is difficult to know just what made one return to France, so great was the fear, the dread of the agonising existence in and around the trenches, after the brief wonder of being back in old England again. On the other hand, the hope of leave did help many a man to hold on to his sanity, although as the war dragged on it was often postponed or completely lost sight of.

Now, near Albert, within less than a mile or so of the lines, a few French peasants were still determinedly endeavouring to exist in whatever remained of their homesteads and villages. Occasionally one might find among a

11

few shops what was left of a bookshop or even obtain coffee and be served by smiling girls or their mothers, who enquired in French if you were well.

'Bonjour Mam'selle,' we would say and nod. 'Comme ça?'

They would laugh, and perhaps the sun would come out from a blue sky, just like the one over Nether Oldston, to give the lie to what was happening not more than a mile or two away, where under the same ethereal blue tinged with smoke and the smell of cordite, the corpses of young men were lying in polluted water-filled shell holes, decomposing beneath clouds of bluebottles.

Among the local people, at first sight, no one appeared to notice the constant thud and whistling of shells. The movement of the table and occasional rattle of the cups was ignored, but if you were watching carefully you might see a twitch of fear on the mam'selle's face. She had perhaps endured the disappearance of a neighbouring village when shells had destroyed friends and loved ones, together with a shop or dairy where she had worked. Occasionally a crashing reconnaissance plane caused great havoc where it fell.

Further back, French towns continued to carry on as far as possible and were full of uniformed men seeking different sorts of pleasure with the knowledge that it might be their last chance to do so.

I once fell into conversation with a soldier in a café who turned out to be a nephew of Mr Marty, the auctioneer from Remsditch at home, who had sold me some of my wheelwrighting tools.

CHAPTER TWO

After I had been in France for eighteen months I was sent to join the staff of a main dressing station, again with Dan Ayris.

One night soon after arriving I was on duty during the arrival of casualties being brought by a string of motor ambulances from different stations. As the hum of our generators coughed and spluttered the lights in the tents constantly flickered, but as the continuous stream of wounded was carried in I became aware, over the noise, of a woman's voice among their attendants. This was not unusual, as many nurses and VAD helpers were working in these primitive medical stations. That evening the number of wounded needing assistance was considerable so the orderlies were overworked and the woman, who was one of the drivers, was helping to steady a man who had lost a leg. Uniforms and heavy clothing in the poor light made it difficult to see more than the bulky shapes of people and I did not recognise who it was in her greatcoat and muffler. So I looked up in surprise from entering the details of a patient when I heard her exclaim 'Abey Staughton! It's you!'

I must have looked nonplussed.

'It's me, Charlotte Purton-Hentis!'

I was amazed to see that it was indeed Miss Purton-Hentis, from the manor house at Nether Oldston.

'I'm over at L'École Car Port. I'll be back again before long. The aid posts are swamped with wounded and we've got to get straight back. I'll come and find you. We could have a cup of tea together. Fancy bumping into you here! You look all right. I see you're a Corporal, too!—Bye then!' and she was gone.

'Come on, Corporal!' said the orderly waiting in front of me with the next patient. 'We'll be here all night!'

I forced my mind back to my task. 'Name, rank and number?' I asked, and automatically filled in the next admittance form.

At 2.30 in the morning my relief arrived and I handed over to him.

As I made my way through the almost dark camp towards my billet, I murmured aloud 'Miss Charlotte!—Did I imagine it?—I need some sleep. It's a bit unlikely.' Perhaps it was my imagination, although Mrs Pickvance had mentioned in one of her letters that Miss Charlotte was away somewhere driving an ambulance.

'What's up Abey? Talking to yourself are you?' asked Dan Ayris, who had been behind me, walking back from the intake area.

'I've just seen a girl from home,' I said.

'I expect so. I see one every night when I close my eyes!' replied Dan.

'No, really. I've just seen her with the ambulances!'

'Yes, I know. You're losing too much sleep, lad. Well, we should get a good three hours now.'

For a week or so I watched out whenever ambulances arrived but there was no sign of Miss Charlotte. I asked one or two other drivers from the same car port but they shook their heads and said they had not heard of her. Nothing was certain in this situation and I realised she might very well have been transferred to another area. Ambulance drivers were a mixed bunch: volunteers from America who had been anxious to help the war effort before that country became officially committed, pacifists, men who had been rejected for military service, a few RAMC drivers, young women from well-to-do families at home who could drive a motor vehicle. As time went by I thought less often of meeting her again. Occasionally when a driver from L'École Car Port came in I mentioned her name but I never found anyone who had any knowledge of her. That is, until one morning when I was collecting eggs from four hens we

15

had adopted. They had belonged to some abandoned farmstead and we had made a run for them and fed them on scraps.

A uniformed man with the familiar red cross on his armband stopped to speak to me. Unshaven and too unkempt to belong to the regular army, he was probably a volunteer from Blighty who had been rejected as unfit for active service. 'Hey, Corporal! Aren't you the one who was asking about some wench called Miss Charlotte with the ambulances?'

'Why yes, that's right,' I said. 'Do you know her?'

'No, but I heard someone else asking about her over there. Her name was Hentis, wasn't it?'

'Purton-Hentis.'

'That's it. She was over at L'École some time back.'

'But not now?' I asked.

'No. But drivers come and go. I'll tell her you were asking if I come across her.—How did you know her?'

'Oh, we came from the same village at home.'

He expressed interest in the eggs I was holding and I gave him one to boil for his breakfast.

I thought no more of the incident until I was summoned to the CO's office two days later.

*   *   *

16

In the wooden structure which served as the Admin. Office and also contained Major Rawston Barnes' room, I was told to keep my cap on when I entered the big man's office.

'Click your heels and give a smart salute,' said the orderly at the desk outside his door. Two sharp raps like those from an auctioneer's hammer were then plainly heard from inside and the orderly tapped the door before disappearing inside. I nervously rubbed each toecap of my boots behind my trouser legs in a last minute effort to ensure their cleanliness.

As I checked my cap for straightness the door opened again and the orderly barked 'Corporal Staughton!'

I shot up straight and entered.

The major sat behind a desk and sitting to my right was another brass-hat. After my salute the major said 'At ease Corporal,' and I tried to relax a little, for it appeared that I was not being hauled up for some unknown offence.

'Corporal, Major Hartley Trott wishes to speak to you,' he said.

I looked across at the slight, uniformed figure, who seemed rather too small to be a major. The red around his hat appeared to weigh heavily enough to cause it to rest very well down on his head.

'Perhaps he's got one a size too big,' I thought in the second or so that passed while I regarded the rows of medal ribbons, the gold pips on his shoulders and the red tabs on his lapels.

His expression was not reassuring but his voice was quiet and cultured when he spoke. 'I understand, Corporal, that you know a certain Miss Charlotte Purton-Hentis of the VAD Ambulance.'

I was rather taken aback by this. 'Er, yes sir,' I replied. Surely even under army law in wartime this could not be regarded as a crime, I thought. Even the regulation forbidding a young service woman to accompany a man on her own at any time was not in question here. Perhaps there had been some confusion.

'I understand you knew her at home before the war.'

'Well yes, sir. I knew her to pass the time of day. She lived at the big house, of course.'

'You would have no difficulty recognising her?' He looked hard at me.

'She's been killed!' I thought. 'They want her identified.' I thought of her sitting up on her father's motor-car in Nether Oldston, waving, and old Jes noticing her smile. I thought of her father in his slippers looking for his cat in the hayfield. 'But wait a minute, majors don't run around like this if an ambulance driver, however beautiful, gets killed on a battlefield,' I reasoned.

He was waiting for my reply.

'I would recognise her, Sir,' I said.

18

He looked across at Major Rawston Barnes, who nodded almost imperceptibly.

'There's a chair in the corner, Corporal. You may sit on it.' After easing the sides of his hat he took it off to lay it on the desk, where it continued to look larger than most hats.

I made as if to sit on the cheap, bentwood chair which was about as far away from the desk as was possible in that small room.

'No, no, Corporal. Bring it over here,' said Major Rawston Barnes, slightly irritably. I did so.

'What I have to say next, Corporal, is of a confidential nature. Whatever the outcome of it may be, you will be bound under the Official Secrets Act to discuss no part of it with anyone.'

'Yes, Sir,' I said.

'Miss Purton-Hentis has been involved with our Intelligence Service. A short while ago she was smuggled further into France behind the enemy lines to meet an agent carrying details of German movements. We believe all went well until recently when her contact man here and his deputy were caught by cross-fire during the initial stages of getting her back. As you probably know, she speaks excellent French and has been able to spend several days in a small community without attracting attention. We have no way of knowing if the position of the two men when killed has alerted the Germans to anything. We need to get her back quickly and our only chance is to take a slightly risky one and send someone to meet her whom she will recognise. We have lost contact completely and so it would be very much a hit-and-miss affair. The two agents who have been killed should never have been at such risk together. There has been mismanagement here, I am afraid, and it has left us to do what we can to get her back.'

I stared at him. I had begun to see why I was here. Charlotte was a British spy and I was being asked to go into enemy territory to pick her up because I would recognise her!—'Is this real? Is it another result of too little sleep? Is this small major with the big hat a product of my imagination?' I wondered. But no; it was real, all right. He was watching me and awaiting my reaction. I looked across at the CO uncertainly. He nodded to confirm what I had heard.

'When?' was all I said.

'Today,' said Hartley Trott. There was a short silence. Then, 'We have looked into your records and are satisfied that you could be sent. Are you prepared to go?'

I swallowed hard. They were not giving me much time to consider. I looked from one to the other. It would be more difficult to say no than to go!—'Yes Sir,' I answered.

'Good man!' said the small major, lifting the large hat once more and lowering it well and truly over his small head.

Outside the major instructed his sergeant chauffeur to take me to L'École Car Port. I was told to report to Captain Shaw. The road followed a devious route round shell holes and over temporary bridges. The sergeant hardly spoke and we reached the transport area without incident.

I was presented to Captain Shaw in the ramshackle remains of a village school serving as the Orderly Room.

'Ah, you're the corporal who's going,' he greeted me. After saluting him I stood to attention while he leant back in his chair. 'Nothing much to it, really. We could have sent anyone but it turns out that you can recognise our agent and that could be useful.' He noticed me standing to attention. 'Oh, at ease, Corporal.—Look, I'll explain the details. Sit down, man and take your hat off. There are some cigarettes there on the desk somewhere.'

I declined the cigarette but sat down.

He found the cigarettes under a khaki scarf and a box of headlight bulbs and helped himself to one. 'Well, as I've said there's nothing much to it, really. None of your fancy spy drama that stories are made up of. It's simply a matter of going to guide this girl back through the lines where it's quiet at the moment, and seeing that she is brought back here without delay. The information she is supposed to have is only going to be of any use if we get it quickly. Also, the longer she waits

21

the greater her danger of being discovered. Late this afternoon a lorry will take you from Caients to meet two sappers about fifteen miles north into Belgium. I will arrange for you to take a horse-drawn ambulance from the CCS and you must drive it to Caients and wait by the church there until the sappers find you. They will lead you on foot through the barbed wire as soon as it gets dark. It is pretty quiet round there at the moment but it is heavily guarded and watched. There is a plan for a raid tonight a little further along, which we hope will attract attention from your movements. A hundred yards or so from the wire will be a derelict church. Just beyond that, along the road that used to lead to the village, is a farmhouse with barns and sheds around it. Go to it. A woman should answer. If anything goes wrong, as you are in uniform you'll be taken prisoner, and you must plead lost or concussed. Purton-Hentis should be inside and as soon as you see her, say "Life is full of surprises". Do not delay. She must accompany you immediately back to where you left the sappers. You will take with you the VAD uniform for her to put on before starting back. The French woman will get rid of the peasant clothing. This will help allay suspicion if you are both caught or killed, as you will appear, what you indeed are, members of our forces that have become separated during casualty rescuing. If all goes well you should be back here tomorrow morning.'

He wrote on a piece of paper and handed it to me. 'Take this to the cookhouse. They will give you a meal. Do not under any circumstances discuss what you are doing with anyone. If you encounter any problem before leaving contact me here. Report back here again at three o'clock. You must keep the rendezvous with the sappers.'

It was now 1.30. The car port was simply a transport depot for ambulances, most of them motorised, with a few mechanics to keep the vehicles running. Tankers bringing petrol to the depot were constantly getting stuck in the mud and shell holes, where they were targets for enemy aircraft machine-gun fire.

I did not feel hungry so instead of going to the cookhouse I wandered about, trying to come to terms with what I had become involved in. For a moment I stopped to watch two German reconnaissance planes flying over low, towards the west; just ahead of me an ambulance was sliding with its back wheels spinning. It slewed round to lurch into a slurry-filled shell crater. As I approached I could hear the cursing of the American driver as he got out.

'Would you believe it! This is the second time I've been in this same doggone hole!'

Inside the canvas-covered back were two men, both groaning quietly as they lay on the peculiarly angled stretchers of the inclined

23

vehicle.

'I'm gonna need a tow.' He climbed up onto the top of the cab and waved to attract a tractor driver, who was employed solely for the purpose of hauling out mud-bogged vehicles.

In the background was the occasional bump and whistling of shells, then suddenly, as the tractor began pulling the ambulance out, a stray shell struck the small group of buildings I had just come from. All was confusion. Fire spread quickly in great sheets as petrol from a nearby tanker flooded out. Figures darted about in the billowing smoke. Cries for help could be heard. I stumbled over a soldier lying in the mud, bleeding badly from a leg wound. I attempted to stem the flow but knew it was too late. He was already unconscious. I ran to help pull out survivors from the orderly room where I had waited to be interviewed by Captain Shaw. Having done that, I stopped, while around me other people were digging, or overloading the injured into the few available ambulances. I was confused and wondered what to do. Obviously it would be difficult now, if not impossible, to report to the captain at three o'clock. I wondered if he had survived. I asked a sergeant if he knew. He did not. I then asked a lieutenant who was directing the ambulance loading.

'Captain Shaw was killed by this shell. What did you want him for?' he asked.

'I was told to report to him,' I answered.

'What about?'

I hesitated. 'Er, I think he wanted me to go somewhere for him.'

'Help with these, instead,' he ordered.

I did so, while I wondered what should be my next step. Major Hartley Trott and Rawston Barnes were the only people I knew who were aware of the mission I was supposed to be undertaking. If I got a lift back to the clearing station perhaps I could contact one of them to find out about the sappers mentioned by Captain Shaw. But I had probably got enough information from him to be able to go ahead, if I could find out where to meet them.

I managed to position myself out of sight of the lieutenant and when an ambulance was full I swung round and into the cab.

'What the hell . . . ?' began the driver.

'I need to get to the CCS immediately!' I interrupted.

'So do these poor devils and I'm overloaded now!' he shouted.

'I'll stand on the side!' I shouted back as he revved up the engine. 'You might be glad of my help!'

'The weight is too much,' he argued.

Fortunately he was a lance corporal and I was able to use my extra stripe. 'Do as I say, Lance Corporal,' I said.

He swore, and let out the clutch violently, nearly throwing me off into the mud and causing the suffering men in the back to groan loudly.

We slid and skidded out of the camp and lurched across the mile or two to the CCS.

The CO was away inspecting billets somewhere and Hartley Trott was not to be found, either. I went to the small vehicle maintenance area and told the sergeant there that I had been instructed to get a horse-drawn ambulance.

'Can't spare anything,' he said without looking up from examining the hoof of a grey mare.

'This is urgent.—CO's orders,' I added.

'Everything's urgent here, Corporal. We can't get 'em out quick enough. You'd need a chit from the CO, anyway.'

I realised I had no written authority, but persisted.

'Look, sergeant major, I've just had instructions from Captain Shaw at the car port, with the authority of the CO here, to take a horse-drawn ambulance immediately. There is pandemonium at the car port from a direct hit on the orderly room, so I can't get written authority from there in time, and the CO here is out at the moment. But my orders are imperative, Secret Service if you like. Ten minutes now could foil an important plan!'

The Sergeant Major stopped buckling up the harness he had just put on the mare. He led me away from two privates, who were grooming horses. 'If you're pulling a fast one,

26

Corporal, I'll have you on a charge when you get back. Give me your name and number. Take that cart over there. They're both fresh horses. Bring 'em back safely or I'll have your guts fer garters!'

I started to say I would not need the stretchers inside but decided that rather than explain this I would let them remain.

I jumped aboard and with a flick of the reins was off. The cart and stretchers rattled as we drove out of the marquee and headed for the road to Caients. The watch my father had given me when I left home for Nether Oldston, seven years earlier, pointed to 3.40.

CHAPTER THREE

To get to Caients I decided to head north-west rather than go back to the car port. The countryside was badly damaged; in this particular part little remained of the road I must follow and there was very little left of habitation. Houses and other buildings lay strewn in heaps of rubble while an occasional domestic creature such as a cow or sheep might be seen wandering about among the tangled broken trees over the pock-marked ground. Captain Shaw had roughly sketched my route as he had described it and I had put the plan in my pocket. No doubt he would have gone over it again more carefully if I had had my second meeting with him, but fortunately it was not complicated and I found what appeared to be the direction for Caients without trouble. The day was heavy with cloud and as the afternoon wore on it looked as though we might have rain. The prospects of moonlight were not great. I was not sure whether to be glad about this or not. I stopped to examine a broken signpost lying splintered in a ditch. One of its arms bore the name Caients so I felt reassured about my direction as the other possibilities were out of the question. As I headed further north-west I neared the front line again and encountered troops marching to take up positions in the trenches.

At a point which I felt must be near my destination I was stopped by a second lieutenant in charge of a party of soldiers. 'Where are you heading, Corporal?' he asked.

'I have an arrangement to pick someone up in Caients.'

'On whose authority?'

'Major Rawston Barnes at Number 7 Casualty Clearing Station.'

'Do you carry written authority?'

'No Sir, but you can check with the major's office on field telephone. I was instructed to move fast and use his name as authority.'

He peered into the back of the waggon. 'Very well, Corporal. One of my sergeants can accompany you into Caients.' He turned to one of the men with him. 'Sergeant Ayreton, go with this vehicle and report back here on its return.'

'Yes, Sir,' said the sergeant, and climbed into the front with me.

I decided that the chances of giving away information that might prejudice the return of Miss Charlotte if I mentioned the mission to the sergeant were minimal.

'I've been sent to pick up an agent across the lines not far from here,' I said as soon as we were on our way again. 'I need to contact two sappers between now and nightfall who are to take me through the wire but I only know that they will be at the church at Caients. I wonder how to find it?'

He looked at me as though I was crazy. 'Gawd knows, mate! I'm amazed that anything can be found in this bleedin' wilderness,' and we rattled on while evening approached.

At a small road junction stood an empty cottage. Half its red tiled roof had gone but its curtains still appeared intact. I pulled up as we overtook the lonely figure of a man pushing a wheelbarrow full of turnips.

He stopped and I said 'Monsieur!' I spread my hands and raised my eyebrows to indicate a question. 'Église?'

He put the wheelbarrow down and for a moment looked puzzled. 'L'église?' he repeated, then as if remembering, he said 'Ah,

L'église à Caients qui est abimée!',
'Oui Monsieur,' I nodded.

He pointed along the road and added 'Ce n'est pas loin, deux minutes peut-être'.

I thanked him in English and drove on into the tiny village of Caients, where its damaged church was used by soldiers as an observation post. The remains of its tower afforded something of a vantage place for such operations.

On my arrival a sergeant asked who had sent me and at the mention of Captain Shaw's name I was introduced to the two soldiers who were to guide me through the barbed wire entanglements. As Sergeant Ayreton was about to lead the ambulance away to find water for the horses I told him I hoped to return before morning.

I had to cross a stretch of no-man's land, which was a morass of mud that heavy rain had made of the shell craters and generally ravaged land between the two armies. Uprooted and grotesque parts of trees stuck up at strange angles and in daylight small flowers, which never wearied of trying to grow again, could be seen among the partly covered remains of dead soldiers and horses. As what must have been the raid mentioned by the captain got under way the dreadful landscape was illuminated by flashes and streaks of light from flares and exploding shells along to our right, and the horizon became continuously lit up where areas of intense battle raged further away.

With mud smeared on my face and hands, wire cutters and gloves in my pocket and clutching a small waterproof bundle of tightly rolled VAD clothes, which I was advised to lose quickly if caught, I was guided beyond the cruel barbed wire and told to head for the spire of a school over to the north, until I came to the remains of the road between Guinchey and L'Acre. I was to follow this road to the left, past what had been a blacksmith's shop, and on to the farmhouse at the bottom of the hill.

'Watch out for snipers, and good luck mate!' said one soldier as I left them and began my part crawling, part dodging, part sliding journey across the mutilated stretch of what had once been gentle green pasture with grazing creatures and quiet woods. To take every precaution to avoid snipers and lookouts would have been absurd in other circumstances but the fear of the immediate bullet and the quick end or the dreaded lingering, lonely death out here kept my attention on the need for extreme care. The experience I had of bringing back wounded from no-man's-land under similar conditions was useful, but now the fact of passing into enemy territory caused my heartbeat to quicken. The task in itself was not a difficult one. As I had been told, anyone could have been sent to do it but the fact that Charlotte would recognise me as a friend in place of either of the two agents she was expecting was an advantage. The danger lay in being spotted or arousing suspicion. It occurred to me strange that it was possible to do what I was attempting and if it was, why was the British Army not doing it and taking over the German occupation?

I proceeded very carefully. My wire cutters enabled me eventually to make a big enough hole to get through the enemy wire without causing more than a few scratches. The gloves and cutters would be tell-tale items if I were caught but I dared not discard them as there was no likelihood of finding my way back to this very place on my return. I put them into my pocket and proceeded in the direction of the road.

Following instructions I had been given, I arrived at the farmhouse.

A woman responded to my knock at the door. I repeated the password and she called Miss Charlotte, who appeared but failed to recognise me with the mud on my face. Her eyes widened when I said who I was and she looked more closely.

As soon as she had put on the VAD clothes she was ready to leave.

We went together back the way I had come. Carefully we picked our way in the flashing darkness. Hardly speaking a word, we left the road to head across the old lines where we began crawling and darting from cover to cover, bush to shell hole, bricks to upturned root. As we proceeded across the morass of wet slime a fine rain began. Although this added to the discomfort and made progress even slower I was glad of the effect on visibility, for just before it began I had seen the first streaks of dawn appearing to the east. But my trust in the weather was broken when one shot and then another sounded perilously close; evidently a sniper somewhere over where the ground rose slightly had seen us. And even in the light rain flashes of gun fire never ceased to show up the stark silhouettes of shattered trees. The rain stopped again, and as a breeze moved the clouds a small moon showed through them, making pale yellow reflections on the wet landscape. Because of the sniper we tried not to be moving when flashes lit the sky but it was impossible to do this perfectly.

We had almost reached the first derelict trench when Miss Charlotte gave a faint cry.

'My God. She's hit!' I thought. 'Are you all right?' I asked.

There was a pause, then she said 'Yes, but he's just caught my leg.'

We slid into the shelter of the trench. There was about eight inches of water in it and it smelt of rotting flesh and dampness.

'Where are you hit?' I asked anxiously.

'Here somewhere,' she whispered, although of course I could not see anything. 'I think it's bleeding.'

The moon came through the clouds again and by moving out of the shadow cast by the side of the trench I was able to make out the dark wetness on her leg that could only be blood.

'It's a bit painful,' she said.

'Let me see.'

She pulled the clothing up. Even in that semi-darkness I realised that this did not look like a slight flesh wound. My heart sank as my hands now became wet with the darkness of blood. I knew how quickly such wounds, if not dealt with in minutes, could take their fatal toll. I tore off my mud stained jacket, then my shirt. With trembling fingers I ripped it into strips. The wound seemed to be just below her knee and, thanking God for my training, if only of six weeks, I was able to apply an effective tourniquet with some speed. I covered the wound with more muddy shirt and gave her a sip from my water bottle.

'I think I'm done for, Abey,' she said quietly.

'Don't say that, Miss Charlotte,' I said. 'Listen, it's not many yards now—we'll make it all right, but I'll have to carry you.'

'No, Abey. You can't do that. You go on and see if you can get help.'

I shook my head, well knowing that the

chances of bringing anyone back here in time to save her were small. It would be too difficult to find her again quickly and time was most important. Every minute her wound remained unattended increased the chances of septicaemia and tetanus.

'I'm going to try.—Come on.'

I put on my jacket. She groaned as I picked her up, using the fireman's lift to put her over my shoulder. It was not the most comfortable position for her but it was the most likely way of getting her back without my collapsing. I staggered from the shell hole, sliding in the wet. She was fortunately not a big girl and I was able to make some progress. I now threw caution to the winds; either we reached our own lines quickly or everything was lost. But I had to stop frequently for breath.

Like a huge brown slug slipping and sliding in the mud I dragged over every stick, stone and shrub.

At first Miss Charlotte groaned if I stumbled and even once murmured 'Oh Abey!' but after that when I stopped for breath she lay silent on my shoulder. I felt no movement from her. Once I put her down and tried to speak to her but there was no response. I could do nothing to rouse her and I felt panic rise within me. I suppressed it and lifted her again. I crawled on, and stumbled into a water-filled hole. I thought I heard a faint sound from her as the cold water drenched us for a moment. After struggling to firmer ground I lay exhausted. It must be further than I had thought. Then I forced myself on.

'Who goes there?' suddenly came the voice of a sentry.

'Thank God!' I murmured, and managed to call 'Friend!—I need help quickly. I've got a wounded girl here!'

There was silence for a moment, then a soldier with a fixed bayonet showed himself.

Apparently along this section of barbed wire, sentries had been warned to watch out for me bringing back a girl.

'Hey Jack!' he called. 'It's 'im all right!'

Jack appeared and between them they lifted and carried her through the wire entanglements. I stumbled on behind them.

'Careful,' I said, 'she's bleeding badly.'

They produced a stretcher and Miss Charlotte was carried slightly more comfortably to safety, where stretcher bearers took her to the nearest aid post.

'Your boots need some polish, Corporal,' joked the first soldier.

Utterly exhausted, I was helped back to see an officer in charge. A second lieutenant, to whom I managed to explain the urgency of getting Miss Charlotte back to base as soon as possible, contacted Hartley Trott by telephone. I also was taken to the aid post where I received tea and was able to dry out most of my clothing. Miss Charlotte was given an anti-tetanus injection and her wound washed and dressed. She remained unconscious.

The sergeant shook his head. 'Not too good, Corporal, not too good at all, but we'll have to move her. Her only chance is if we can get her back to base hospital.'

Two bearers were detailed and after a quick attempt at drying and wrapping her in dry blankets while I continued drying myself and exchanged my soaking tunic for a greatcoat, probably taken from a dead soldier, we began the journey back to the church observation point. From there, a motor ambulance took us whence I had started. I was given a bath, a meal, some fresh clothes and, after a brief interview with a captain who had taken over from Captain Shaw, was told to get some sleep. I asked about Miss Charlotte but no one seemed to know anything.

The next morning I reported to the CO. He gruffly said it was a great pity that the girl had been hit. 'She's still unconscious and we need the information that she's got.'

'Do you think she will pull through, Sir?' I asked.

'Can't tell. You know the chances, Corporal. Anyway, see the sergeant out in the office. He'll give you a chit to take to stores and get some new kit. Report back to duty after you've had some sleep. The medical section are under pressure again from last night's action but when it quietens down put in for a forty-eight hour pass and I'll sign it.'

Eventually, I discovered where Miss Charlotte was, but the tiny screened-off ward in the officer's section of the primitive canvas hospital was kept strictly guarded and no visitors were allowed.

The conditions around that ward remained unchanged for the next twenty-four hours. 'At least she must still be alive,' I reasoned.

A little later I was helping move a stretcher case that had just arrived when a sergeant said 'Miss Purton-Hentis is asking to see you, Corporal.'

'Miss who? . . .' I began, then 'Oh, is she?!' I exclaimed. 'Right, I'll go as soon as I've finished here.'

Miss Charlotte was sitting up in bed in the tented cubicle. She looked pale but was quite bright.

'Oh Abey, it's so good to see you!' she exclaimed.

'Are you all right?' I asked.

'Yes, I'm fine. Got a stiff leg, though.'

'How bad is it?' I said.

She looked serious. 'There are soldiers out there every day in raging battle lines who want a Blighty wound more than anything. I go out across a derelict bit of comparatively quiet territory and land one straight away!'

'Are they sending you home, then?' I asked.

38

'Yes. I'm fed up with it. I've only been out here a couple of months. Just beginning to enjoy myself then Bang! and I'm to be bundled off home!' She tried to pull the wooden box serving as a bedside table a little nearer but it was obviously hurting her leg. 'Oh blast it!' she exclaimed impatiently. 'Abey, pull that damned table a bit nearer will you!'

I moved it.

'It's quite bad, then,' I murmured.

'Oh, I don't know! It's bound to be a bit painful for a day or two. Mostly I can't feel it. It's stiff and all bandaged up so it's difficult to move with it. The fact is, it was difficult enough to get out here in the first place, being a girl. They certainly don't want one now with a duff leg.'

'Did you manage to get what you went over there for?' I asked.

'Yes. I've related all the information to our friend the major. He said it was a good job done. What he did not say was that I am now a throw-away piece of equipment, like a used shell case.' She sounded quite bitter.

'You'll get patched up better in Blighty than you would out here and, anyway, they're saying it'll all be over in a matter of weeks.'

'They've been saying that ever since it started, Abey. Here, don't stand there like that! Sit on the bed. The Germans seem to have got all the chairs! Daddy will be furious when he knows I've got a duff leg. He was furious about my coming to start with. He wanted me to stay in that hospital at home.' She looked serious again and added 'I expect I'll wish I had if they take my leg off!'

'Oh come on, Miss Charlotte! That doesn't sound like you,' I said, not quite knowing what to say.

'Will you be going back to Nether Oldston?' she asked suddenly.

'Yes. I hope to. I had almost finished my apprenticeship.'

She stared at the blankets on the bed. 'I suppose you'll have to, then,' she said in a way that made me feel very boring.

'Have you any plans?' I asked.

'I don't know. It's so difficult being a girl. I'd really like to do anything that girls really don't do.'

'Like what?'

'Oh, car racing, flying my own aeroplane, leading an expedition somewhere, anything with a bit of go in it!' She looked at the opposite canvas wall and stared as if into the far distance. I felt the sad frustration of her hopes. It was possible for a girl to do any of these things but only if she battled with convention and if her family was wealthy. I could see she was fearful of her chances now, if her leg wound was to be disabling. Only time would tell, and during the next part of it she would be confined to long hours with her thoughts and wishes.

'When are you leaving?' I asked in an attempt to change her line of thought.

'Probably tomorrow,' she said in a dull voice.

'I'll come and see you when I'm on leave,' I said.

'Oh yes Abey, do that! You'll be my only contact with my great adventure!' Her voice turned slightly bitter and her eyes again glazed over. 'My great adventure.' She gave a hollow laugh. 'Fantastic! A spy in France for three days! Exciting!' Then her voice softened and she looked at me. 'But Abey, you know, I did love that ambulance driving with those skidding wheels and sliding about in the dreadful mud. Those poor men, the blood, the dark French roads and the flashing sky. I loved it Abey, away from smart clothes and polite hypocrisy. They should have left me doing that!'

I did not interrupt.

'I wouldn't have missed that for the world. I loved it!' Then after a few seconds of silence she added wistfully, 'Marvellous!'

I stood up. 'I must get back,' I said.

She nodded.

'I'll come and see you when I get back,' I repeated. '—Give my regards to your family,' I added formally.

She took my hand. 'Thanks Abey, thanks for bringing me back. God bless you!' She pulled me towards her and kissed my cheek.

41

I smiled, and mumbled 'Have a good trip back and God bless you, too.'

Outside the tent I plunged back into reality.

'Get that load of medicines organised, Corporal!' barked the same sergeant who had given me the message from Charlotte. 'We've dealt with all those stretcher cases while you were away!'

CHAPTER FOUR

'Let's go to Tresville tomorrow,' Dan said. It was three o'clock one morning of the summer of 1918. We had just returned to our bell tent from duty and were practically asleep on our feet. We had been given twenty-four hour passes to start from 8.0 the next morning. I rolled out my mattress. The night had not been very dark and now dawn was already breaking. Light was coming through the tent walls as we crawled into bed.

'All right. I doubt if I've got enough money to exist on, but if I wake up again before this war's over, we'll go!' I said.

Next morning on getting up we washed in the old tin bowl that was kept for the purpose and struggled with our razors to remove the stubble that never seemed affected by lack of nourishment. We expertly went along all the seams of our underclothes with a lighted candle to remove the ever-present lice before putting them on again and after a quick visit to the cookhouse for the usual porridge, bread and jam, set off.

'Lucky we were to get away!' murmured Dan as we climbed the part-broken fence at the back of the camp. 'I saw old Bengers watching us in the cookhouse. He's probably gone to check what we're on this morning. If he had thought we'd got a pass he'd have found a reason for cancelling it!'

Cow parsley, daisies and cowslips covered the sides of the road as we walked away from the camp. It was difficult to believe we were not in England. Before us lay the French countryside; rolling farmland green with patches of brown, a thatched cottage here and a red tiled roof there.

Dan was older than me by four years and had been an articled clerk to a surveyor in London. 'All right for folks like you, all this green stuff,' he would say in his strong Cockney accent, waving his hands over the landscape. 'You don't know any better, young Abey, but I wasn't brought up with straw in my ears. Sophisticated I was, before this bleedin' war. Boots like these—' he glanced down at our footwear—'I'd only ever seen on men digging up the roadway when our drains were blocked. Now, if my eyes are open I see them everywhere and if they are closed I dream about cleaning them!'

We came to a main road where motor lorries and carts were passing continuously. We waved at everything that passed and eventually a meat lorry returning from the front line picked us up. The back did not smell too good but it was better than walking. Once or twice we were slowed down or brought to a stop by columns of men marching in different directions. We could hear one lot whistling the usual tunes long after we had passed them and as the lorry rattled round bends and bumped along the worn road surface the breeze picked up a few odd words from 'Lily of Laguna'. But mostly the columns marched silently, the men looking tattered and exhausted, their NCOs often dragging along at the side with heads down.

When we reached the small town of Nantles, we left the lorry. I knew Dan was hoping to see a girl he had met here some months before. She had written to him once but she spoke very little English and after having to ask old Maggie, a sister at the hospital, to translate it for him, he had given up. Now we went to the café where she worked and, after a shy smile and slow response, Dan persuaded her to meet him after lunch when she told him it was her 'Half day, this day!'

We walked round the town, which was full of soldiers doing what we were. There was an air of unreality about it all; life was trying to ignore death. Everyone had become used to

'The War' and there was a weariness beneath the cheerful surface that was the result of over three years coping with fear and uncertainty. Friendliness was everywhere, yet temper and irritability were often thinly veiled. Shops seemed to have plenty to sell although prices were very high. There was a picture palace with posters outside advertising an English film starring Charlie Chaplin and Mary Pickford. Public bars had been quick to multiply to cater for the demands of the troops and a flourishing casino now stood in the middle of the town. Here, men who were embittered by war and ready to respond to their fleeting and perhaps only opportunities of wine, women and song, could spend their money in an attempt to blot out the 'for tomorrow we die' feeling that lurked within us all.

'Come on Abey! Let's have a look in!' said Dan.

'We haven't got enough cash,' I said. I was wary about entering. Army lectures had warned against these places and posters as well as general insinuations made one very aware of the existence of 'the pox', even if uncertain of all the methods of picking it up.

'They don't charge to go in and I'll buy you a drink,' he said.

'We can get a drink at that bar over the road.'

'Come on, Abey. Don't be so dreary!' He

was half through the doorway and I followed him in.

Inside it was smoky and crowded. There was a buzz of conversation and an accordion was playing somewhere. Groups of uniformed men stood around. Some sat at tables. Everyone was drinking or smoking. Occasionally voices were raised and there was laughter. Girls danced and sang in a small space in the centre and acted as waitresses between acts. We edged our way in and bought 'Deux biers, Mam'selle,' from one carrying a tray of beer. Dan winked at me while we stood sipping the overflowing glasses as they dripped onto the crowded floor.

I thought of Charlotte. She would be back in England now, probably back in Nether Oldston. It was difficult to believe that Nether Oldston still existed. Even now, I thought, the doors of the workshop might be open and old Ben, Harry Teemer and the others wheeling out a waggon from amongst the shavings. What was reality? I pondered. Why did I not just go back home? What was I doing here in France? Would this nightmare go on for ever? I thought of old Henry's face when I had watched him over the bench . . .

'Come on Abey, drink up!' said Dan, nudging my arm.

'Sammy Blofield had been killed before I joined up,' I said aloud.

'What?' said Dan, amongst the hubbub of

noise around us.

I shook my head. The accordion was playing 'Two little girls in blue'. I thought of Jim Stringer, who had been playing it on his gramophone only the week before, when he had told me he planned to get married on his next leave. A stray shell had blown him to pieces the next evening. The record was still on the gramophone when someone had taken it away . . .

'Abey, come on!—Look, there's a couple of chairs by that table.—Are you going to drink that beer?' I followed him to the table, where the empty glasses rattled occasionally as the building shook from the heavy guns not far away and, to remind us further of what was going on outside, low flying aircraft vibrated plaster from the ceiling.

'What will you do while I see Michelle?' asked Dan.

I shrugged.

'You could go to the cinema,' he said.

I nodded. We sat and watched the dancing. A soldier sleeping soundly at our table slowly slid lower and lower. His friend, who had his arm round the waist of a pretty girl sitting on his knee, laughed at him but after a while he slowly sank onto the table himself. With a little smile at us, the girl slipped away to join the next table.

A loud explosion suddenly rocked the building and a small hole appeared in the roof, sending slates and plaster crashing down into the crowd. There was some shouting, girls screamed, everyone stood up, and the accordion stopped playing. For a moment the crowd seemed to hesitate. Panic was imminent. The eyes of those I could see, except for the drunken and sleeping, were wide. There followed a moment's silence, then the accordion began again, everyone began to talk and sit down again and the tension passed. A number of people who had been hurt by the falling masonry were carried or helped out, but life had become so uncertain that the laughing and drinking and rough amusement continued, while the small bright blue piece of sky at the hole in the ceiling shone down through the heavy haze of tobacco smoke.

Outside, a little later, it clouded over and began to rain. Michelle did not turn up where we had arranged to meet her and Dan went to look for her. I walked along the streets rather aimlessly and continued until I reached the outskirts of the town. The rain had stopped and white clouds were now high in a blue sky again. I could see a few buildings clustered together in the distance and I decided I would walk as far as them before returning to the town to look for food. As I neared the buildings I could see that one was a wheelwright's workshop. Outside, an old man wearing a white apron nodded to me when I stopped to look, but then he ignored me while he piled up some oddments of timber to fill a hole in the nearby hedge, where a large white goat was trying to push through it.

'Just in time!' I remarked rather pointlessly, except to say something. I detected no smile under his ragged grey moustache and he made no reply; then, after giving the precarious structure another push at one end, he went over to the open doorway in the workshop. He disappeared inside and all was quiet. The whole place looked derelict, with grass growing over the front hard area. A big, heavy waggon stood silent in one corner with green moss showing underneath it, and corn sprouting from damp areas between its floorboards. Hens pecked about in various places and I thought of the brown Leghorns at Hardwick's. I went to peer through the doorway. It was so gloomy that at first I could see nothing. Then the same man appeared, so close to me that I jumped in surprise.

'Pardon, Monsieur,' he muttered, and made as if to close the door, which would not move: obviously it had not been closed for a long time. He gave up, and stood blocking my path into the shop. 'N'entrez pas, Monsieur. Le magasin est fermé.'

I spoke no French, but it was obvious he did not want me in there. 'I am a wheelwright, Monsieur, I am interested,' I said, and indicated I would like to look, trying a few French words I had picked up to mean 'look' and 'friend'.

He did not move but went on shaking his head, 'Non, Monsieur, non!'

No one else appeared to be there so I shrugged and turned away, but then stopped near the big waggon and stood looking at it, in the vague hope he might see I was interested. Nothing happened. I headed towards the road and glanced back; he was still standing in the doorway. At that moment a big mongrel dog came racing from the road into the overgrown forecourt, pulling on a piece of string tied to his collar and held by a young girl on a bicycle, with long lengths of bread sticking out from her coat. She was flushed with the excitement of her ride and was calling to the dog to stop, while small stones shot out from her skidding wheels. The dog rushed over to me, dragging the bicycle over sideways and causing the girl to hop on one leg to keep upright.

'Raoul! Raoul!' she shouted.

When they reached me the dog stood wagging his tail, while I held the handlebars and she got off.

'Merci, Monsieur', she said, smiling and talking both to the dog and me in fast French. Then she stopped and, looking harder at me, said in English 'Ah, but you are English, Monsieur. Do you speak any French?'

I shook my head. She lay the bicycle down where it was then, handing me the bread, untied the dog's collar. It went over to the old man, who was still standing in the doorway.

'Marie! Viens ici!' he shouted.

The girl waved to him.

'Marie! Viens ici. Vite!' he shouted again.

She called back to him then, noticing a magpie sitting in a nearby tree, exclaimed 'Ah, la pie! Toi creature horrible!' and, siezing a stone, ran towards the bird, hurling it and making the big black and white bird fly off. She came back to me and took the bread. 'Have you been to see my grandfather, Monsieur?' she asked.

I shook my head. 'No, I was just walking past. I am a wheelwright and was interested in looking at the workshop.'

She looked across at the old man who was shaking his head.

'Viens, Marie!' he called again.

'My poor grandfather. He does not trust visitors. He has had everything stolen and his men have gone to the war. There is no work here. He is ashamed to let you see. I am sorry, Monsieur. I wish for the time when you are the wheelwright at home.'

I wondered how old she was. She looked almost unreal with her sparkling freshness, her smile and her neat, clean dress. Her English was almost faultless. I felt loath to look away from her to the drabness of the surroundings, and to have to walk back into the war-torn town and the everlasting nightmare I had come from.

'Your English is so good,' I said.

'My grandmother taught me. She insisted. She would only speak to me in English. "Everyone that matters speaks English," she used to say to me when my grandfather was not listening.' At this she smiled again and took my arm. 'You come and have the coffee. It will be hot and refresh you.'

'What about your grandfather?' I asked.

'He will not mind.'

We walked past the old man and she led me into the house, which adjoined the workshop.

'Sit down while I pour the coffee,' she said and took down three mugs from a dresser. A coffee pot was keeping hot on a black iron range. She took a tin and sprinkled a handful of ground coffee into the already strong black liquid. She poured it out and then pushed a cup towards me. She took a mugful out to the old man. While she was away I looked round the kitchen, dark and silent. The scrubbed table was bare but the room was tidy and the glowing coals, although low in the range, gave a warm, red glow, which reminded me of Maisie Hawtin's maiden aunt Fitzy Bluebottle's hot cider at home. Sparse and bare though the homestead was, I was moved by the homeliness of it. The faint warmth on my knees from the range, the hot cup in my hands, the kitchen and the contact with this caring, enthusiastic girl were all worlds away from trench warfare and army life. I felt very self-aware while I sat drinking the coffee. It was black and very bitter but I went on sipping it. Marie returned and sat facing me while she drank hers.

She smiled over the top of the mug and I smiled back. 'Does your grandfather work out there?' I asked.

She shook her head. 'Non. He sits there guarding his tools. He mends a neighbour's barrow or perhaps a hand cart but non, he waits for the war to end. He knows also that the things he makes are becoming—how do you say it?—out of date?'

I nodded. 'It is the same at home,' I said. 'We have the motor-car and the iron wheels, but there will still be much work for all the wooden wheels.'

She shrugged. 'The world is changing. Men and women see different things. New ideas are coming. I know more about today's world than my grandpère. He is holding onto the past but it is no good. I tell him to come out and get ready for the future.'

'How old are you, Marie?' I asked.

'I am nearly fifteen!' she said, as if it were a challenge.

'To be beautiful and wise at fifteen is very unusual,' I said.

She looked at me to see if I was serious. I was, and she poured more coffee to hide a trace of self-consciousness.

'Come, I will show you the wheel workshop,'

53

she said, putting her mug down and opening the door at the back of the kitchen. The earlier rain had now completely cleared and high clouds were almost still in a fresh blue dome. I could hear the rumble of heavy gunfire not very far away and was reminded of my world, waiting for me to re-enter it.

The old man was chopping fire-wood inside the workshop and ignored us when we entered. It was quite large inside and although littered with the paraphernalia of wheelwrighting was bare and lacked the living craft. There were no waggons there but as I entered I smelt and felt the ghosts of past wheelwrights. The old man watched me. I picked up a jack plane and he stood up. I looked down its sole to sight the cutting iron, then placed it on its side as I had always been taught, back on the bench. He relaxed slightly.

'We had eight men here before the war,' said Marie.

I nodded. We walked on until I stopped at a bench, picked up a piece of cleft ash, found a wooden spokeshave and, after tapping the cutter roughly on the edge of the bench to adjust it, crudely began to make long curly shavings from the piece of ash.

Marie laughed and called to the old man, 'Regarde, Grandpère!'—but he made no response.

'Come, we will go for a walk. It is too nice to be in here,' said Marie, and led me outside again.

I raised my hand to the old man before leaving but he ignored it.

Behind the buildings the land sloped down to a railway track and Marie began to walk alongside it. I followed her.

'I hate the war!' she said without looking at me; and then after a pause, 'I said I hate the war!'

'I heard you.'

'Do you hate it?' she asked.

'Yes, I suppose I do.'

'Surely you know if you hate it or not!'

'I'll be glad when it's over.'

'Have you got a fiancée in England?'

'No.'

'What will you do when it is over?'

'Go back and be a wheelwright.'

'Grandpapa says that the wheelwright is finished.'

We walked on until we came to a row of open trucks standing on the line.

'How often does a train come along?' I asked.

'About twice a day, mostly to carry troops. Sometimes supplies,' she said and climbed up into the first truck. She held out her hand to me and I followed her. An old tarpaulin was stretched across one end of the truck and the sunshine on it made the corner underneath warm enough to sit under it.

'Not as comfortable as it might be!' she said,

'but it is wartime.'

We sat in silence for a while, listening to the distant guns. A low flying German aeroplane circled twice overhead and I thought for a few moments it might decide to attack the trucks, but it went away.

'Why are you here like this?' I asked. 'Is there anyone else living here with you and your grandfather?'

Marie shook her head. 'Non. There is no one else here. My grandpapa is not really my grandpapa. They found me, he and my grandmama, in the hay barn. I was left there as a baby.' She stared ahead at the side of the truck then after a brief pause said, as if to herself as much as to me, 'I don't care though! Babies are often not wanted!' Then more gently and looking down at her hand, 'Grandmama died last year.'

There was a silence and she turned away so I could not see her face.

I was startled by the emotion in what she suddenly said next: 'It's all such a waste of everything! All the good things are wasted! They are trampled on, they die, they are pulled apart, blown to pieces! I often wish they had not found me in that barn!'

I glanced at her. Her eyes for a moment burned with fury but then she looked at me again and gave a little self-conscious half smile. Again, in those harsh surroundings, she seemed so soft and gentle. I dared to put my rough, army-khaki-clad arm around her. As she responded, snuggling into my side, my heart beat faster.

How long we lay in the corner of that truck on those hard floorboards I do not know, but I do know that in the limited privacy under the sagging tarpaulin I was overcome with an emotion of great strength for this lovely uninhibited young girl, who seemed to represent the part of life that my savage world had turned away from. The nearness of her soft warmth, her gentle voice and delicate touch released pent-up longings within me that the brutality of war had made me forget. But, in spite of all its unnatural harshness and the enforced life of unbalanced masculine discipline, I had not until now railed against the war. Now, for the present moment I was prepared to lie here for ever. Reason and reality melted away. The warm sun on the old, dilapidated tarpaulin created a corner of heaven within the railway truck, while its damp floorboards dried out, creaking feebly from time to time in the private quietness of our little world. The gunfire in the distance was blotted out by the intoxication of the young girl in my arms, as we lay breathing the scent of the old, drying tarpaulin above us.

Marie murmured to me in her own language and I kissed her long and passionately. They would have to fetch me back to the army, I thought. She and I would make our way to a place where no one would ever find us. I could never go back to my bell tent and the war.

Time seemed to have disappeared, until we were startled by a train on the next track to ours. It went slowly past with troops packed into its open trucks while we huddled further into our corner, pulling the tarpaulin down further lest we be seen.

Somehow the spell was broken by this and after the train had passed we crawled out and watched it disappearing along the line.

We climbed down onto the lines again and for a few moments stood holding hands. Then without a word being spoken we turned back towards the homestead.

I helped Marie feed the chickens and watched her milk a poor-looking old goat whose udder was so near the ground that only a flat pie dish could be put beneath it to catch the milk. We smiled at each other and touched hands, then she said we would make a meal. I realised that a lot of time must have passed and wondered what Dan would be doing.

'My friend will wonder where I am,' I said.

Marie smiled.

'I must go to tell him where I am. I will come straight back.'

She smiled again and shook her head.

'Why do you shake your head?' I asked.

'It is goodbye,' she said sadly.

'What do you mean?'

'You do not return.'

'Of course I will!' I insisted.

She smiled and turned away towards the back door of the house. I ran after her and held her arm.

'Marie, I'll be back very soon and we will eat together. Will you wait?'

She looked up at me and there were great tears in her eyes.

'Marie, why are you so sad?'

She shook her head. 'Life is not like you think Abey. Great evil forces are at work in the world.'

'But Marie, I love you.'

'And I love you Abey, but the world will take over again in a little while and it will pass. I would wait, but you will not return.'

The sun was very low now and I wondered what Dan would be doing. The old man stood watching me as I hurried towards the road. I waved to him but he ignored it and went on watching.

'I am coming back, Monsieur!' I called to him, knowing full well that he could not understand me. Before I hurried round the bend in the road I glanced back; he was leaning a piece of rough timber against the place he had previously filled in the hedge, where the goat was pushing a way through again.

The light was getting lower when I got to the town and I wondered if I might not be able to find Dan.

Two men had upset a market barrow near one of the public lavatories in the market square and the commotion attracted my attention. Dan was there, and about to become involved. I nudged his arm.

'Ah, Abey. What are you doing?' he asked.

'I'm not coming back to camp,' I answered.

'What do you mean?'

'Just that.'

'Where are you going?'

'I'm just not going back.'

He looked at me, then led me away from the group in the market place. 'Put me in the picture, Abey,' he said.

'I've decided not to go back to the army. I've had enough.'

'What will you do?' he asked, as if this was all quite normal.

'I've found somewhere to live,' I said.

'You have?' he said indulgently.

I nodded. 'It's a wheelwright's place up the road.'

'Is there a girl there?' he asked.

I glanced at him and saw he was looking hard at me. 'Yes. But that's not the only reason.'

'But it is one reason, then?'

I felt slightly less sure of myself. 'So what?'

'Nothing.' He put his hands in his pockets and began to whistle tunelessly.

The group round the market barrow had dissolved.

After a minute or two he said 'Well, I'm going to start back now. It might take till morning to get there. There'll be more chance of a lift if we go before too late.'

'I'm not going back,' I said.

'They'll fetch you.'

I shook my head.

'Of course they will. They know where to look.'

'I've had enough, Dan.'

'So have I.' We stood looking at each other. 'Come on Abey. Let's get off.'

'I told you I'm not coming!' I insisted.

'Don't be so stupid! They'll find you and shoot you for desertion. Think of your mother. Get a hold of yourself and stop it!'

He was beginning to lose patience, but I was determined. He turned away and began to go towards the road leading out of town. Then, stopping and turning round, he said 'We can come again.' I stared at him as if I had not heard.

He walked back and put one hand on my arm. 'Come on Abey. This isn't like you.'

I pulled away. 'It'll go on for ever,' I said.

' 'Course it won't! A few more weeks and we'll be home. You can come back here then for that girl if you want to! When I had chicken pox and thought it would last for ever and that I would never be able to go out to play again, my father told me of a poem he had learned as a boy. It went something like:

61

"Be the day weary or be the day long,
  At length it ringeth to Evensong."'

I showed no response and after another
pause he turned away again. 'I'll wait down
here for ten minutes, then I'm off!' he shouted
over his shoulder.

I watched him go out of sight, then turned
in the opposite direction to walk slowly and
somewhat uncertainly back through the town
again.

It was now dark and I decided to head back
for the road where I had walked before when I
had found the wheelwright's. It was not so easy
as I had thought. Not knowing the town and
being in the dark, I was confused. Then at one
point when I stopped near a small grocer's
shop, three soldiers approached me.

'Are you Corporal Abraham Staughton?'
one asked.

I was surprised he knew my name. 'Yes,' I
said.

'I've instructions to take you with us back to
the hospital camp.'

'You can't,' I said.

'Want to bet?' he said, and one of the others
laughed.

'Who are you and who sent you?' I asked.

'Come on, Corporal. Never mind the
questions! Let's get going.'

'I'm on a pass. I'm on my way to visit
friends!' I said indignantly.

'Come on,' said the same soldier, ignoring what I had said.

I did not move.

They waited.

'You have no right...' I began.

'Corporal, we are living in a time when rights are not always respected. Walk along with us or we will carry you,' I was told.

I stood for another moment in the dark street glaring at them, then I turned and tried to make a dash for it. One of the men was anticipating this and I was stopped before many yards.

'No one minds you running, Corporal, but it must be in the right direction!' he said as he grabbed me.

I knew I was beaten and was furious. I was forced to walk with them out of the town and along the dark road back towards the hospital camp. After a while a horse-drawn waggon stopped beside us and I was lifted into it and held firmly as we rumbled on over the poor road surface in the direction of the most frequent flashes and gunfire.

CHAPTER FIVE

By the time we reached camp it was nearly morning. I was almost asleep on my feet but still seething with the indignity of being handled like this. The three soldiers who had forced me back were all corporals. I did not recognise them, and when we climbed out of the cart they marched me into the guardroom to report back from my pass.

Outside, one of them gave me a heavy slap on the back, which nearly knocked me over, and said 'No hard feelings, mate! Get off to bed.'

They disappeared into the gloom of the tents and sheds. The sky lit up with an enormous explosion not far away. I stood confused and cold. Then my anger turned to extreme and painful loneliness. I walked back to my tent. In the heavy gloom I could hear Dan's breathing in the next bed to mine. He was fast asleep. I knew, of course, that he had sent the three corporals but I bore him no grudge. I pulled a blanket over myself as I lay on my bed fully clothed and with my boots still on. I felt empty, devoid of all thoughts. I shivered under the blanket, staring up at the dark canvas above until I fell asleep.

I awoke in the morning after only a few hours. I found I had removed my boots while asleep and wished I had taken my clothes off, too; I felt unrefreshed and very tired. I followed the usual routine as if programmed to do so. That morning I did not speak to Dan, who I felt was watching me closely, but this impression soon wore off.

Back in the wards it was easy to go on,

avoiding any depth of personal thought, although I was conscious somewhere within me of a very heavy heart. But at night, and for many nights afterwards, before sleep my own thoughts resurfaced and I lay awake thinking about Marie, resolved to go back and find her again very soon.

Another push at the front caused another flood of casualties and for two weeks we were working day and night. Then I received a posting back to the regimental aid posts at the front. This depressed me further. I felt I was going back to certain death: no doubt I was being sent to replace a casualty and I wondered how I would cope this time under fire.

Dan knew how I felt and I saw the look in his eyes when I told him. 'Bad luck mate,' was all he said.

On the morning of departure I shook hands with him before climbing into the motor ambulance with my few belongings. We had not mentioned the episode of our return that night from Nantles but I knew it was in his mind, just as it was in mine, while we stood there, stuck for words. We had become real wartime comrades and were going to miss each other.

'Thanks for what you did that night, Dan,' I managed to blurt out.

He slapped my arm. 'Sorry about it, mate.'

We both knew he had done what was best. I

never saw him again and often wondered if he survived the war.

The ambulance was going to pick up casualties near the front line. A stretcher bearer who had been injured and was returning from sick leave in Blighty was travelling with me.

'Like coming back to a bad dream!' he said as we regarded the mutilated landscape over the canvas doors of our vehicle. The road disappeared and the engine moaned when the driver put it into low gear to bump and roll across the rough terrain until we reached the pick-up point, where stretcher bearers were waiting with their wounded.

We helped load the stretcher cases into the ambulances, then, as the ambulances turned round to return to the hospital camp, we set off with the bearers, who directed us to the base area to report there, while they headed towards one of the aid posts.

Captain Charles Maltby was the medical officer in charge and his staff had been depleted recently when a shell killed four of his orderlies. He had two aid posts, one very near the front line about five hundred yards from this base area where we were to live, and the other further along the trenches.

'I thought they would send me more than just you,' he said, regarding me and the private. 'You'll have to go in charge of Post Four, Corporal.' This was the nearer of the two posts.

I nodded. 'Yes, Sir. Shall I go there now?'

'Of course. You're not here for the tennis! Put your stuff by one of the empty beds; there's usually tea in the urn, get yourself a cup. Corporal Mason is in there somewhere. Tell him you're going and ask him to see you get some grub. Don't send anything back here that you can possibly deal with. I'll get round to you when I can. Good luck!—Oh, take that can of carbolic with you. Water is short as usual. Be sparing with what's there; I'll get some more over to you.'

The whole place had been dug out of the ground and was divided roughly into a tiny area for medical staff and a slightly bigger one for the casualties. Covered by pieces of canvas held up on poles, it was damp and dark. I found Corporal Mason. He was dragging a bed out from the staff side to use for an injured man. All the rest, about twelve, were lying on stretchers.

'Have that one,' he said nodding towards a bed frame when I asked. 'You won't spend much time in it if we go on like this!'

I dumped my belongings on the iron frame. Immediately he called to me: 'Give us a hand here, Corporal!'

I helped him get a man, who was unconscious and wrapped in a blanket, onto a bed. I noted the dark stain on the ground where he had lain.

'He's next for the ambulance, if he's still with us,' he said.

The various wounded were lying and sitting crowded together. An orderly was moving between them, passing a water container round. It was a grim sight. Stretcher bearers arrived again and we helped to move the next ten men out, to be carried to the place where the ambulances should arrive again soon. Two more men were brought in from the trenches, one carried in unconscious on a comrade's shoulder, the other minus a forearm with a tight tourniquet of canvas strip wound around his upper arm, which he was clutching. Soaked in congealing blood, his grey face splattered with mud and dark red, he half tottered as his helper set him down. Fear and delirium alternated as he muttered and stared. Captain Maltby and the corporal set about cutting away the part of his tunic above the wound. The congealed tourniquet was removed and a new one put on. The arm was washed in strong disinfectant. The man began yelling. The doctor nodded to Mason, who administered morphine, turned to examine the unconscious man and then back to me. 'Get away to the aid post as quickly as possible, Corporal. I'll be over to see you before morning.'

Corporal Mason called over to tell me where to find rations to take with me and I hastily drank some strong, warm tea. Another orderly was told to take me to the aid post and return without delay. I waited momentarily at the entrance while a man who had died earlier from his wounds was carried out for burial. The captain followed the bearers out, taking a tattered prayer book from his pocket as he did so.

The aid post, or Post Four as we called it, was dug well down into the earth. Sandbags formed its walls and its tin roof was held up by rough pieces of timber that acted as beams to carry the weight of earth shovelled upon it. It was all built into the trench system, where two front line operational trenches met. Its sparse equipment included two chairs, an enamel bowl, a box of bandages, iodine, tourniquets, enamel mugs, blankets, morphine, syringe, soap, towel, primus stove, methylated spirit and paraffin. There was also a field telephone.

Here I met Sergeant Chisholm. He was lighting the primus stove to boil a kettle and when I introduced myself he held up a hand. 'Waait a minute, man,' he said in a strong north country accent as he peered round and under the boards set into the sandbags to form a shelf-table. 'Ee, here it is, look!' he said, picking up a primus pricker and buttoning it into his tunic. 'I can't afford to lose that, you know!' He regarded me. 'So you're the lucky lad who's been chosen to rule the famous Post Four! Come inside and I'll give you the lowdown on its mysteries.'

The orderly who had accompanied me

wished me luck and left to return to base.

'Things have quietened down a little now again; it's been pretty impossible just lately. You'll have Alf Murcott here to give you a hand. He's a good lad and he knows the ropes. He's along fetching water just now.'

The kettle boiled and he brewed some very strong tea. Without milk it was indeed bitter. I thought for a moment of black coffee and Marie.

'The great thing is to keep things moving. If you don't you'll be jammed up suddenly with wounded. Wash them, stop the bleeding, give them strong tea, bandage them and if possible send them back along the line. Bad cases: get them back to base. I'll see the stretchers keep coming if I possibly can. I won't forget you're here. The Doctor's all right when you get to know him. He's seen some action. He needs a rest like all of us, but it's not likely at the moment. There's no nonsense with him and his temper does not improve. Anyway, don't lose heart, man.'

He gathered up his small pack and stuffed a notepad into it with a blackened clay pipe and some tobacco. 'It'll all be over one day and you'll be sitting there at home showing your campaign medals!' He smiled. 'Oh yes, the colonel is said to be coming round in the morning. He's not a man to reason with. He'll criticise whatever you're doing. Take no notice. Just say, "Yes Sir," give him a smart salute and he'll go away again.'

He touched my arm. 'Au revoir, Corporal. See you at the base, or in Heaven.'

CHAPTER SIX

I was asleep on one of the chairs with my head on the workshelf when Alf Murcott shook me. 'Hey Corp, wake up, it's over. The war's over!' He shook me again. 'Do you hear? The war's over. Wake up! I've just heard!'

I sat up. 'Over?' I mumbled. 'What's over?'

'The war! The bleedin' war. It's over! We'll be goin' home!' He slammed his clenched fist into a sandbag in the wall and the damp, hessian weave broke to let a trickle of sand run down to the floor. 'Yippie!' he yelled.

We looked at each other, then both looked through the doorway to the trench. It was impossible to feel anything except a sort of unreality. I thought of Mrs Hardwick coming into the workshop and saying 'Sammy Blofield's been killed in France'.

Two men carried a sergeant in and laid him on the floor. He had been shot through the chest. The bullet had entered cleanly, as usual, and torn out through the back. He lay unconscious and groaning, as we cut away his tunic. Murcott pointed to the blood around his mouth and shook his head. I nodded. I gave

71

him morphine. We cleaned him up gently, but there was nothing we could do to stop the bleeding.

A second lieutenant came into the post and said 'The war's over, Corporal Staughton. We have had official orders to cease fire at eleven o'clock but to remain watchful and make no contact with the enemy. The news will not be known everywhere for some hours. There may still be some wounded coming in.'

It was now 9.30. I looked at the wounded sergeant. I felt for his pulse. He had died. I thought of his family somewhere in England, who would be hearing about the armistice before they would hear of his death. Peace, desirable as it most certainly was, had been too long coming to inspire real celebration for many people.

So it had ended. There was a sense of relief but now, and as time went on, I was conscious of wanting to weep. There was disappointment at the anti-climax of continuing in much the same way as before, apart from the shelling and shooting, for what seemed like a long time. News came through slowly but while we awaited further orders, wondering if it was a permanent cease-fire or if the war would start again, food supplies improved considerably. Newspaper copies from England were passed round eagerly and we slowly learned that troops were at last being demobilised. Ex-miners and anyone to do with coal mining were being given priority, to get that industry fully productive again. Troops were withdrawn from the trenches, staff from dressing stations and casualty clearing stations returned to base hospitals, and the regimental aid posts closed. The sick and the wounded were all at last sent home while we awaited further orders, transport and a boat back to Blighty. I had time to think about Marie again.

During that period it was easier to get short passes out of camp. One day some friends were going to the town where I had met Marie and I went with them. I found my way to the wheelwright's house. It stood dejected and totally silent. There were open gaps in the hedgerows and no sign of goat or poultry. I walked past the workshop to the house. The back doors were all open. A window in the house bumped on its stay in the slight breeze. I tripped over a milking pail with remains of milk dried hard at the bottom. Rats scurried away as I stood listening. In the workshop dust covered everything. Sparrows flew in and out of a broken window. The shavings I had made that day all those weeks ago were still on the bench with the spokeshave I had used, its blade red with rust. I stood for a few moments in the eerie silence, conscious of the still guns in the distance, and peered again into the open, deserted house before walking back to town.

At a small grocer's shop near the outskirts I

enquired if the man spoke English.

'English Monsieur? Ah, non.' He turned and called into the back room to a woman who came out, drying her hands on a towel.

She regarded me enquiringly. 'Bonjour, Monsieur, I speak the English a little.'

'Bonjour, Madame. Do you know what has happened to the wheelwright and his daughter, Marie?' I pointed in the direction from which I had come.

She looked concerned. 'They were your friends?' she enquired.

'I met them when I was here before.'

'Ah.' A customer came in with a huge basket to collect bread. She led me aside. 'The sadness is in that place, Monsieur. It is, er, how do you say?—Er, dreadful!'

I waited and watched the big dark eyes expressing her emotion.

'You have just been there, Monsieur?'

I nodded.

'The old man, he is still there. You would not see him. He stays in the house. He is silent, he hides. The girl, Marie, she ran away with a soldier, an Englishman. It is heard they go to Paris. Your Army, er, how do you say? They continued him, non, non! They seek him, er, they follow him. He is the deserter. They find him. He shoot Marie dead, then he shoot himself.'

She watched for my reaction as I absorbed what she had told me. After a moment she put a hand on my arm. 'You come in and have the coffee, Monsieur,' she said and led me through to her kitchen.

I sat silently while she poured the black, strong liquid for me. She moved her face into a smile and again put a hand on my arm. 'She was very pretty girl, full of life and joy like 'erself, La France. Now it is the time for the sorrow, Monsieur. Our country is broken. The war it is over, oui, but the wartime sadness it cannot be ended.'

Two photographs of young soldiers in French uniform stood on a sideboard near her. I did not ask about them.

'The old man?' I asked, swallowing a little of the bitter coffee.

'Marcel? He lies upstairs and waits to die. You go to see him? Non, Monsieur.' She shook her head.

I finished the coffee and stood for a moment after thanking her for it. She grasped my hand with both hers before turning away and setting about her laundry work.

CHAPTER SEVEN

So, here I was! Suddenly it was over! The waiting, the mud, the danger, the dying, the massacre, the noise, the flashing, the smells, the rats, the lice, the bully-beef, the ration biscuits, the tents, the kit inspections, the barbed wire and the ever-lurking oblivion had finished. I was on the train home! Quiet it was, swaying along with two elderly ladies sitting reading on the other side of my compartment. They glanced at me from time to time. It was obvious from what I was carrying that I was a returning soldier, and from their expressions I sensed their warm approval. Through the carriage windows I could see the English countryside. It was raining and although the sky was heavy with grey cloud it was the landscape of Heaven to me. It was nearly three years since I had left and now it all seemed like a dream.

My father met me and I was taken to be hugged and spoiled by my family for ten whole days at the old farmstead before deciding the time had come to return to Nether Oldston and the wheelwright's trade.

As I regarded the countryside from the train which carried me to Remsditch my thoughts were crammed with indescribable mixtures and fragments of memories. A certain heaviness of heart, accompanied by a locked-in awareness of man's baser nature, did not prevent a feeling of excitement from welling up in me as I contemplated arriving back in the village. I stepped from the train. The station was just as I remembered it. No one else got off. There was a moment of silence after I had banged my door shut. The guard waved his green flag and blew his whistle. The engine gave a tiny hoot and began to glide silently forward, before the first steam piston erupted its cloud of whiteness, while the driver leaned out of his cab to wave to the level-crossing keeper, who was waiting to open the gates and let a small horse and cart go over the line.

Albert Hardwick was talking to the ticket collector. 'Good to see you, lad!' he said as he took my bag and I handed over my ticket.

He had brought the dogcart; it looked smart, and Jiffy, three years older now, looked well. I rubbed his nose before climbing in. Mr Hardwick appeared about the same, although his hat was obviously three years older. He seemed quite excited and fussed round me as if I were some celebrity.

'You'll find a few changes,' he said, 'but not many. I've got a new lad. Started just after Christmas. He was going to live with Mrs Pickvance but when she heard you were coming back she refused to have him. Said the room was yours, till you said you didn't want it!'

I smiled. Mrs Pickvance had written to me regularly all the time I was away so I had been kept up to date with most of Nether Oldston's 'goings on'.

Later she told me that the night when I lay buried and unconscious for a while Eva had made a continuous whining for those exact hours. Mrs Pickvance had had to sit up through the night with her and told me that she had feared the worst for me.

On my arrival she greeted me with tears and a big hug. I thought of when Sammy Blofield had first brought me to meet her and how he and I had laughed so much at her reaction to the cow muck on my coat. How innocent and carefree those days now seemed, locked away on the other side of the war!

'Where's Eva?' I asked.

She did not answer immediately but went to put the kettle on, then laying her hand on my arm, said sadly 'She died, Abey. Six months ago. I didn't tell you in my letters because I thought it would upset you. She was nearly fifteen and I found her in her basket one morning. I think she missed you all the time. I always told her when I was writing to you and her ears used to prick up at the mention of your name.'

Horace was not at the workshop when I arrived.

'He's not too good,' said Jes Beales, one of the carpenters, when I asked about him. 'His breathing is bad.'

All the men greeted me like a hero and I met Bertie, the new apprentice, a small, shy boy who looked as if he should still be at school. His big white apron hid him completely, apart from his head and boots, as it wrapped right round him to overlap double at the back.

After he had seen me he quickly went outside, to continue trying to make the pump work.

Albert Hardwick led me into his office. I guessed he had had a major tidying up operation recently and Mrs Parsons, who helped at the vicarage, was even then dusting the desk.

'Thank you Mrs Parsons, that will do nicely for today,' he said, and noticing my obvious surprise, went on 'We've had a bit of a clean up, Abey, and Mrs Parsons is going to help us keep it like that.'

I smiled at her.

'I'm glad you're safely back, Master Abey,' she said, putting her dustpan and brush in the cupboard and taking off her apron.

As the door closed behind her I asked 'What about Pip? Young Pip Horner?'

Albert stopped pulling out his chair from behind the desk for a moment, then said with surprise, 'What? You haven't heard, then! He was killed just before the armistice.'

I was taken aback. I was somewhat used to hearing of men being killed but I did not know that Pip had even been called up.

Albert sat down. 'Ah, poor young Pip! A good lad, too. No business to have gone. He kept on about going, then suddenly off he went. Put on his age and before his mother knew what he'd done he was in the army, sent to France and within a week or two was killed.'

'Good gracious! I hadn't heard. I am sorry! I liked Pip.'

'Ah well!—There it is, lad. War's a rum business. His mother's taken it badly. They say she can't accept it. She's still taking some sort of sedation. You and Perce Chennel are the only ones who have come back to the village. Will Auger's boy, George, died of pneumonia before he even got to France and Morris Bagley from up at Lonestock was killed on the Somme. Jake Pooley died at Gallipoli.'

I nodded. Then, 'What happened to Miss Purton-Hentis?' I asked.

'Ah well, poor girl! You know she was wounded?'

I nodded again.

'Well, she came home and no one quite knew what had happened. She was something to do with ambulance driving with the VAD but there was talk of her getting mixed up in intelligence: you know, spying and that.— Anyway, she went back into hospital and now she's lost the lower part of her leg.'

'Oh!' I said, visualising that vivacious smile of hers and not able to think of her as disabled. '—Have you seen her since?'

'No. No one has, really. They say she won't leave the house.'

He shuffled some pieces of paper. 'You'll be working with Harry Teemer and old Ben, now. There's plenty on at the moment with the

80

waggons. Mind you, it's not what it used to be. We're still building carts and making wheels but it's a diminishing trade. Since you went the motor-car and its metal wheels have been a-coming. Old Abe, the blacksmith next door, has even got himself a motor. Sits up there he does, proud as a peacock and drives it out at weekends. Straps that little grandson of his on the seat next to him and off they go. His missus won't go near it. Bang, bang it went last Sunday afternoon when I was just dozing off after Sunday dinner.'

I had become used to the motor vehicle, as its use in the army was almost total by this time, and I said 'I expect we shall see an end of wooden wheels.'

Albert shook his head. 'Ah maybe, maybe.— But if we ever do, it will be because of man's inability to make 'em properly. They'll never match a well-made wooden wheel for purpose or for beauty.'

'They're not economic nor practical for the pneumatic tyre, though, are they?' I asked.

'Well, perhaps not for the motor, but they'll match up for anything else, and for the rutted old farm roads they're better!' he declared firmly.

I discovered that Bertie had only been at the shop a week and that Albert had got him on trial because his mother had implored him to do so. His father was a merchant-seaman and the boy was beginning to prove a handful for her. Albert told me he was planning changes through the workshop as Ben James was going to retire in about a year.

'When he goes, Abey, I want you to be in charge of the waggon end. Young Simon Gathercole has developed into a good man. He's working on the waggons now so we should keep our numbers up when Ben goes. In the meantime, I want you to work all the time with Ben. You know his ways. We'll not see a better wheelwright than him and I want you to be able to do anything he does afore he goes. I've told him, and he's expecting you to join him. I'll keep my eye on Bertie. He's a bit too quick at everything. Needs watching at the moment. I'm not sure about him yet, but you'll have nothing to do with the stock work now.'

I was pleased to hear of my upgrading, but the contrary human nature within me needed to assert itself and I felt a twinge of regret that I would not have a reason for going out to see Magnolia or mess about in the field or stable during the working days ahead.

After a brief nod when I went to join them, Ben and Harry carried on as if I had only been away to do a job for a few hours.

After I had installed my old tool kit in a corner and put on my apron I found myself rounding the straight strong grain of some riven oak spokes. It was nearly three years since I had picked up a spokeshave to use seriously but it felt natural enough again in my hands. For a fleeting moment I saw the red rusted spokeshave on Marie's grandfather's bench. As I got into the swing of the work I found my mind querying my action, for I had grown away from the discipline of the craftsman. I was aware of a restlessness within me. The existence of a front-line soldier in wartime is one of crude restlessness. One moment he is in the turmoil of battle and another he is resting behind the lines, where life is lived from minute to minute and importance is attached to nothing. The quiet, slow-moving workshop scene, with its dusty stacks of timber and its unquestioned standards, the unhurried men with their lunch bags and sandwiches, instead of being the reassuring, desirable life I had long dreamed of from the trenches, now seemed unreal. The hours seemed monotonous and I longed to get outside. I found my concentration almost non-existent. Even when talking, I lapsed into never-ending memories from anguished France and of the faces of men now gone. I felt strangely lonely. There, although I had often been plagued by fear and the desire to be doing something else, I had been strongly motivated by the necessity of the moment and the hope of coming to the end of it. Aware of the futility of his lot, a soldier on active service comes to terms by living superficially. His moments leading from one action to another can only be accepted if his mind is not involved. Also, I had tasted what now seemed a greater freedom to observe and consider what I saw as life itself on a grander scale.

Often in the heat of battle and in quieter hours of duty abroad I had longed for this old workshop and its life. Now, again at my bench, surrounded by all I had dreamed of, I was conscious of a discipline I had not been aware of before. I was expected to get on with these spokes for the rest of the day. Why, in the knowledge that I was free from the army, was I not whistling and enjoying my creative craftsmanship? Oh, I was grateful enough for my deliverance and would be for my lot in future, but where was the joy I should be feeling at the rolling-off of these shavings, from the scent of the new oak? What had happened to me?—I stared at the spokeshave in my hands until in my mind's eye the landscape of the Somme drifted before me. The face of a mutilated soldier I had turned over in a muddy shell hole, the bright eyes and white knuckles of a young boy recruit before he went over the top in a bayonet charge, a heap of old greatcoats taken from corpses and awaiting transport passed before me.

'We be a-waitin' fer them spokes, Abey lad,' said Ben's voice.

I was jolted back to the realities of Nether Oldston. I nodded, and proceeded to shape the pieces of oak with more resolution.

'Are you still making those dogcarts?' I

asked Ben.

He shook his head without looking up.

'Not a lot now. We still get the odd one to do but folks be on to the motor now.' He paused, then finished drilling out a felly before laying his brace and bit on the bench and taking the curved piece of ash from the vice: then he added, almost as if to himself, 'We made a tidy few, though. Ah, we did fer a while.'

His big moustache had become completely white in my absence and I wondered if he had trimmed it at all in all that time, so bushy and unkempt had it grown.

'Mornin' Abey,' called a voice through the front doors.

I recognised the voice immediately and I looked up to see Fitzy Bluebottle or, more properly, Betsy Harbottle. 'I heard you were back. What's it like to be out of uniform?'

Albert Hardwick appeared and tried to head her off as she came across the workshop. 'Now Betsy, we've got a lot to do this morning and Abey hasn't got time to talk.'

'Don't you be so mean, Albert Hardwick!' she said, walking round him. 'I've come to welcome one of our soldiers back. Fancy you trying to stop me! What ever would your poor old mother have said?'

'Hello, Miss Harbottle,' I said as I continued removing the shavings.

'Like old times, it is!' she said, standing

beside me. 'I better not take up Albert's precious time, but you call in to see me when you've got a minute. You look well. I expect you've been enjoying yourself with those Mademoiselles from Armentiers!'

She swept out past Albert without looking at him, then seconds later came back to remind Harry Teemer that he had not returned a cider recipe she had lent him.

It was hard settling down. Sometimes very hard indeed. It had been late spring when I returned to Nether Oldston but winter weather continued well into May and June. I took to going for long walks across the countryside, not because I wanted to walk but because I needed to be alone and to look out across the landscape. I felt a strange link between the fields and hedgerows, the grazing cattle, trees and streams with those whose memories were a part of me. This was the land that they had dreamed of, longed for and died for. Yet often I felt detached from my surroundings. I needed to come to terms with my homecoming without them; as it was I felt unable to accept the consummation of my return. I could not make it matter whether I reached the workshop at the right time in the morning or if what was not done today was left until tomorrow. The need to earn a living had become unreal.

Each time I walked past Oldston House I wondered about Miss Charlotte. At the end of my first week back I had decided to go and enquire after her.

One was not expected to walk up to the front, just like that, and I certainly would not have contemplated it before acquiring a little more confidence than I had before my time in the army.

One day I finally went to call. A manservant whom I did not recognise opened the door. 'One moment, please, Sir,' he said when I enquired after Miss Charlotte.

Inside, I could see a polished oak table with a round silver butler's tray on it. Somewhere a door slammed and I could hear one of the big dalmations barking leisurely.

The man reappeared. 'Miss Charlotte is much improved now, thank you, Sir, but she and the family are all away at present. Good day, Sir,' he said in a monotone, and closed the door.

CHAPTER EIGHT

The drain on working horses over the war years had been considerable. Thousands had been conscripted from farms and businesses all over the country while motor waggons and vans had been produced almost exclusively for the armed forces. The lack of horsepower, equine and mechanical, was an important factor in the everyday life of the countryside. Wherever possible breeding mares were being used to produce without delay, although the gestation period of eleven months was not a factor which enabled anything to happen quickly. Nevertheless, on Trows Farm, Greg Mottram had been allowed to keep his two young Suffolk Punch mares for breeding, and from the services of a visiting stallion both had already produced some fine foals, the oldest of which were now two years old. Both mares were now with new foals.

Greg's father, old Seth Mottram, had bought the two young fillies at a sale a year or two before he died. He never told anyone how much he had paid for them but locally it was said they were of too good a breeding for the needs of Trows Farm. But Seth had had his own ideas and was a man who delighted in good horseflesh. Towards the end of his life he had decided that the money he had accumulated under his mattress would still be there when he no longer was, so one day, without a word to anyone, he had pulled out some of the notes and set off for a horse sale two counties away. He returned a few days later, having walked home with the two fillies. They were his pride and joy during his last days as they took prize after prize, first at small local shows and then at the Oxfordshire County Agricultural Show.

Greg himself had now become interested in

88

these horses and was getting enquiries for them.

He was in the workshop one morning to collect a wooden harrow that had been repaired. 'Come up and have a proper look at them, Abey,' he said when I enquired after them. 'I'm thinking of getting a stallion. 'Tis too far to keep bringing the one over from Middlefeatherton.'

'Doin' very nicely, is our Greg!' said Ben Steel after he had gone.

There was a long pause, while he helped George Groom lever the trestles supporting a waggon body out of the way to make room for a seed drill being brought into the shop.

'Just for a couple of days,' said Albert Hardwick, sensing the opposition to bringing it in while the big waggon needed room all round it.

'We can't get round to put them plates on till it be gone,' said Ben, nodding irritably at the place where the pieces were waiting for fixing.

Albert took no notice, knowing there was plenty of other work to be done on the waggon that could be got at during the time the seed drill was being repaired.

When all had settled again Ben continued. 'Those 'orses 'is dad got are makin' 'is fortune now.'

Beyond the workshop, in the part of the field where a covered area had been made for waggons, a new circular sawbench had been installed during my absence. Twenty-four inches in diameter and the first saw of its kind to come to the area, it was at first something of a novelty. Although the inherent suspicion of any new 'automatic' piece of equipment prevented any of the older men from enthusing about it, the principle of cutting big pieces more quickly and with less effort was attractive. Anything that produced results more quickly and without the special skill of hand and eye caused uneasiness and a sense of insecurity among the men. The fact that it eventually eliminated riving, the process of splitting wood along its grain, which produced a piece of maximum strength throughout its length, supported Ben's pronouncement that ' 'twill spoil standards'. The passing of the old methods of construction and the increase of mass production were against the need for riving, which in the wheelwright's methods was both quicker than hand sawing and essential for durability of wooden implements and, in particular, for wheel parts such as spokes and dowels, sometimes called trenells or tree nails.

The increasing production of metal items that would once have been made from wood and the awareness of the increase in metal wheels, plus the news of the tractor being used instead of the horse, with its implications for a trade geared to the production and maintenance of agricultural equipment, prevented enthusiasm for the installation of the new saw.

Albert Groom and Jes Beales, both fine craftsmen, had become involved with the use of the sawbench and when a session of sawing was about to be dealt with they would move the various pieces of cart and farm implements which had accumulated round it and bring the timber to it. This all took time as the timbers, although not of enormous dimension, were very big and heavy, requiring levers and rollers and sometimes a hand from other men.

The first cut down a log was still done on the pit saw as the sawbench was not equipped to hold and guide a round log. Once a flat face had been produced it could be pushed over the rollers through the spinning noisy saw. Just as important as the sawbench itself was the stationary engine that powered it. Looking back, I wish we had kept it, for it was beautifully made from hand-produced castings. Painted bright green, with its brass and gun-metal bearings gleaming, after starting it chugged soothingly on and on. When being made ready to work its wide leather belt was pushed over from the idling position to the driving wheel by a length of beech kept handy for the job. When a big piece of oak was thrust onto the saw the heavy belt connecting it to the engine, about three yards away, flapped up and down and the note of idling would, after a momentary silence, pick up as the mechanical governors adjusted the engine to cope with the task. Black exhaust would shoot out during this adjustment but when the wood was sliced right through it would drop back to ticking over again, to await the next demand upon it. Its two-stroke mechanism never tired.

Mrs Bannister, whose husband was employed on the LMS railway, lived in the cottage on the other side of the field, not more than fifty yards away from where the sawbench had been installed. Apparently she had been round to complain about the noise of it on a number of occasions. Now, as I stood watching Albert putting some four inch ash through it, I could see her leaving her doorway and making in our direction. Albert looked at me and raised his eyebrows while he inclined his head in her direction.

There was a lull in the sawing while Albert moved some other pieces nearer.

'Where's Albert?' I heard her asking.

Albert Groom shook his head and pointed to me.

She came over to me.

'Where's Albert?' she shouted as the sawing started again.

'He's gone up to Lonestock,' I shouted back.

'What?'

'Gone to Lonestock.'

'Where?'

'Lonestock!'

She took my arm and led me out into the field where she could make me hear better. 'I've told him about this noise! Tell him Bernard's coming round to see him about it if he doesn't do something. It's putting my hens off laying. They go into their little house when it starts and don't like it no more ner I do!'

'It doesn't seem to have affected the hens here,' I ventured, 'but I'll tell him.'

She looked at me in silence for a minute, then said 'I thought you weren't seeing to the hens no more, and anyway I don't want none of your lip. Tell him I'm not putting up with it no longer and that's final!' With that and a firm shake of her finger, she went back to the road gate and home.

I shrugged as I passed Albert, who indicated to me to help pull the timbers through.

When we had finished, as he shorted out the engine and it came to a stop, he said ' 'Tis noisy, but it's not as if we was a-using it all day and every day. 'Ees talkin' about puttin' a bit more roof across fer the waggons now as we're a-using this 'ere fer sawin' '.

Along the road we could see a barrow-type implement being pushed towards us.

As we walked round to the front of the shop Albert stopped and waited for it to arrive. ' 'Tis ole Fred from up at Halfroot. I seed 'im last night in the Barley Mow and he said as 'ee wuz a-bringin' 'is ole seeds barrer down.'

93

Fred arrived. He was a man of about fifty and as his heavy hobnailed boots crunched on the gravel and echoed on the stone forecourt he nodded to Albert.

The seeds barrow was a sort of wheelbarrow which carried a twelve foot long, narrow box arrangement across it. A simple mechanism caused the main wheel, when pushed along, to turn a long rod carrying small brush wheels inside the box, or hopper. When full of fine grass seed, trickles of the seed were sprinkled out through tiny holes all along it. The long box part could be turned round for transportation.

'We're a-waitin' fer it,' he said, without taking the old brown clay pipe from his mouth. 'Wheer d'you want it?'

'Leave it there, Fred. We got a lot on at the moment.'

'I'll look in agin this afternoon when I've finished, then.'

'Won't be done b'then, Fred.'

'What?'

'Won't be done b'then.'

'Termorrer, then.'

'Waal, can't make no promises.'

'I'll look in termorrer. We be a-waitin' fer it, see? Seed beds be all a-ready and weather's right.'

'You should a' brought it in before, Fred,' said Albert.

'What? Didn't know t'was broke till us tried

it. 'Ow could we?'

Albert shook his head and we returned to the workshop, leaving Fred to re-light his pipe before setting off back to Halfroot Farm.

*   *   *

During my time away I had seen the growing use of the metal wheel. In everything that indicated progress the iron wheel was used. With the large demand for the motor ambulance in 1915 in France, when the retreat from Mons and the crossing of the Marne were seriously hindered by the inability of the horse-drawn ambulances to remove the vast numbers of wounded quickly enough, the wooden wheel remained on the battlefield only on the already existing waggons and gun carriages. One evening when I had been waiting on the outskirts of a French village for a pretty girl who in fact never turned up, I found myself leaning against a wrecked and abandoned twenty-five-inch gun carriage that was lying half on its side in a ditch near the road junction. As it lay with one wheel uppermost I noticed how heavily constructed it was. My wheelwright training was both offended by its appearance of clumsiness of proportion yet attracted by its degree of strength. The wheelstocks or hubs were made of metal and the straight cylindrical ash spokes were socketed into them. Metal sockets were again used between the spokes and wooden fellies. Fellies had metal plates between them and the heavy iron tyre, about three inches wide, was bolted right through the fellies. Obviously they were made like this to produce a strong wheel that could be constructed in great numbers without the skill of the true wheelwright.

The weight of such wheels required great horsepower to move them through the mud and heavy soil of northern France.

'Come on, Abey. You be a-dreamin'! Albert wants us to go up to Halfroot and look at the water-wheel. Put your tea bottle in your pocket. We shall be gone for a while.' Ben James had come over to me while I was still spokeshaving, so absorbed in my thoughts that I had not noticed him.

'Oh, all right Ben; how are we going?'

'We'll take Magnolia, 'cause we might need a few levers and things. Sounds like it's broken and will need takin' apart. Bring some cold chisels, a sledge and that there crow-bar over in the corner. I'll get the oil and spanners. Put the jack in and a couple of trestles.'

When I rattled a few pieces of cow cake in the feeding bowl, Magnolia came over from the far corner of the field, followed by Jiffy. I gave them both a couple of pieces and put the halter on the mare. It was good to smell her strong horse scent. I could almost feel my own nostrils dilating, like the mare's herself, as she sniffed at the cow cake in my hand. I had noticed a trace more greying round her eyes but apart from that she was no different and still the boss when it came to food. If jiffy showed signs of pushing in he received a quick nip on the backside to remind him of his station.

I put her in the shafts and loaded up. Along the village we passed Mrs Maycock. Within hours of my moving back to Number Three, The Green she had been pointed out to me by Mrs Pickvance. A distant cousin of the Gathercoles, apparently, and described as 'a very determined woman'. Just what this meant and if it applied to all her fields of activity I was left to find out, for Mrs Pickvance finished by saying 'She's only been here six months but most folk who've had anything to do with her would agree with me'.

I thought I noticed Ben Steel staring very straight ahead as our cart reached her and that she regarded us as we passed her. 'That was Mrs Maycock, wasn't it?' I asked after we were out of earshot.

'Ah, it was,' said Ben.

'Where does she live?'

'Next to poor old Sloan Carter,' he said.

I nodded, and we both looked over the hedge at a fine flock of sheep grazing with their lambs. Most of them were well across the field but as our noisy iron-shod wheels crunched past and Magnolia blew down her nostrils, a few of them that were close to the road shot away quickly, while the mare bore us nearer to the sheep's owners at Halfroot Farm.

I was surprised to find the entrance to Halfroot had changed since I had been there last; it now looked very prosperous.

I thought I recognised a figure gardening by the house; sure enough it was Tapper Chalk, who had previously worked at Lonestock for Maisie Hawtin's father. I went to have a word with him while Ben looked for the farm manager.

'You come back then, boy,' he said as he straightened his back and took out of his mouth what looked like the same old pipe that I remembered from before the war. He went to his jacket, hanging on a spade handle, to find his matches. The heavy clay, sticky from recent rain, stuck to his boots and made him walk very slowly. He talked all the way to the spade and all the way back but I only heard what he was saying as he returned to where I was standing.

'Ah well, Mr Hawtin's place closed down, you see. Sent 'im to jail they did. I 'eard they needed a good man up 'ere so I come up on me bicycle and Mr Pearson Grantle, 'ee was still 'ere then, jumped at the offer I made 'im. "Start right away!" 'ee says and I did. I stayed there and then, ah, and I bin 'ere ever since, not countin' Sundays, that is.'

Ben came into view, talking to the manager.

He waved to me and I led Magnolia over to him. We were taken down a path to the waterwheel. It was quite a small affair as waterwheels go, turned by a stream that had been narrowed to increase the speed of the water at that point. The wheel turned a crusher in the adjoining barn, where grain was rolled and prepared for horses and cattle. It had stopped turning because one of its sections had become dislodged due to rot. The wheel was now unbalanced and the water, flowing only over its lower part, foamed white and noisily as it cascaded over the motionless wooden structure.

'Time it was done away with,' the manager was saying. 'Miss Daphne wants it to be repaired, though, so there it is.'

Ben nodded and stood looking at it.

The manager turned to me. 'We shall get an engine before long to run the mill. Seems a waste of time to put this right but she wants it doing.'

The wheel was about eight feet in diameter.

'We shall need a 'and ter get it 'ome,' observed Ben, as if he had not been listening.

'Can't you repair it here?' asked the manager.

Ben shook his head. 'No. It will have to be done proper or it won't last five minutes.'

'Seems ridiculous to repair it.'

'Ah, so you said.' Ben stood for a moment as if waiting for the manager to be more positive, then added 'Waal, make yer mind up. Do you want us to do it or don'tcher?'

The manager shrugged. 'I've got no option. You'll have to do it.'

'Right. Then we shall need one of your flat waggons, as it's too big fer our cart, and about four strong men for a minute or so.'

While the manager went to arrange this we got down into the water, which was about two feet deep just there, and stood the cart jack on some big pieces of stone, to use as a form of lever, to lift the weight of the wheel from its bearings. The end of the iron shaft that turned the grinding gear inside was square in section where it was fitted through the wheel stock. In the past the wheel and the centre connection had received a coat of hot tar from time to time, not as often as they should perhaps, because to do it meant stopping the wheel while one half dried out, was coated, then half turned and the process repeated for the other half. Nevertheless, the amount of tar caked over the stock and shaft was considerable and had to be cut away with a cold chisel and hammer before we could find the pin locking them together. Once this was removed we set about levering and driving the wheel from its square axle.

When the men arrived they were told to stand in the water and be ready to take the wheel as it was finally dislodged. There were complaints about the coldness of the water after gaiters, boots and socks had been removed and trousers rolled up above the knees.

'I don't see Mr Eli Manager Jones preparing to take the strain,' remarked one or two of the men sarcastically.

'Eli Jones take the strain?' echoed another in mock incredulity. 'Why, he couldn't tie 'is boot laces up again!'

The water was cold and my feet and legs became numb in the water and out of it in the fresh breeze, while we eased off the wheel.

'Steady, steady, here she comes!' said Ben.

The men stood ready with arms already supporting the heavy wheel.

'Here she comes!' he said again as I levered it the last quarter inch. Supported now by the men scuffling in the water as they sought to get their feet steady on the stream bed, the wheel was lowered into the channel where it was then bumped and turned and hauled out by all of us, until it stood leaning against the stone walling of the mill. Someone produced a couple of four-bushel sacks and legs and feet were briskly dried.

Socks, boots and gaiters were replaced and the men stamped around to restore their circulation.

While this had been going on the manager had brought a waggon and Tapper Chalk to help with the loading.

'That makes seven of us,' said Tapper. 'We

need another one. Four each side of the waggon.'

'You 'old the 'orse, Tapper,' said Ben. 'Three's enough each side.'

With the six of us lifting, it was not difficult to walk three each side of the waggon and place the wheel overhanging the sides. The men departed.

'We'll put the rope round 'er,' said Ben.

'That won't move! Don't need no rope round it,' said Tapper.

Ben went on putting the rope around one side and threw it over and across to me to do the same.

Tapper walked back towards the road with Ben and the waggon but stopped for a moment to re-light his pipe. I caught him up with the cart.

'Put me behind, that has. Shan't get them broad beans in afore nightfall now,' he said as the familiar blue smoke, although just as densely produced as ever, was quickly dispersed by the cold wind. As we left him to go back to his gardening he shouted, over the noise of the cart wheels, 'Time old Albert got hisself a motor van. Sight warmer than they old carts.'

Back at the workshop the water-wheel was lifted off by most of the workforce available and set down on trestles in front of the shop and left to dry out in the wind. Bertie was told to take the waggon back to the farm.

All the while we were getting the water-wheel off the waggon and onto the trestles Albert Hardwick was talking to Cyril Parsons, whose wife now kept the office in reasonable condition. He was a local smallholder and they were discussing the possibilities of replacing a wooden axle on his dung cart.

' 'Tis difficult to find the right piece of timber for it,' Albert was saying. 'We've got nothing suitable. Well, we haven't put a wooden axle on anything for years.'

'But it's still a good cart, Albert. I don't want t'lose it.'

'Quite right, Cyril: it is a good cart but you'd do better to let me put an iron axle on it.'

Cyril frowned. 'But t'will need new wheels then.'

'Ah, so it will. But these have done you well, now.'

'I can't afford new wheels as well,' persisted Cyril.

'Well, let it be for a bit. I'll see if I can find someone with a piece of suitable stuff. Although by the time we've done that and made you a new axle it'll cost you more than the iron one.'

Later he asked Ben if he knew where there might be such a piece.

'I'll ask my brother t'call at Strattons and see if they got anything,' said Ben.

What was required was a piece of beech, hewn from the heart of the tree, bone hard and yielding eight foot of six inches square. Although earlier carts and waggons had been produced with such axles, it was now very difficult to find a suitable seasoned and hardened piece as the coming of the iron axle had stopped such baulks being prepared. Like the wheelstocks, they required careful selection and to be turned over and checked regularly, throughout their long period of seasoning.

CHAPTER NINE

Maisie Hawtin visited her Aunt Betsy from time to time, as she had done before the war, and it was while accompanying her aunt to church one evening shortly after Easter that I encountered her. From where I sat near the back I saw her enter and sit in her usual place. Simon Gathercole came in from the tower where he had been ringing the bell and sat next to me. Maisie was still as beautiful as ever. I had often thought about her while I was away and wondered if I had imagined her beauty. I wondered if perhaps, after seeing so many girls of all degrees of prettiness during my time in France, she would appear less striking. But no, my doubts in that direction disappeared as she entered the church, dressed simply, in a blue coat (for the wind was still cold) and a pale straw hat with blue ribbon. She smiled at Arthur Bourton and thanked him as he handed her her aunt's prayerbook, which was kept in church to save carrying it each time. I wondered what had happened to her father. I knew from what Tapper Chalk had said that his yard had closed down.

'What happened to Mr Hawtin?' I whispered to Simon.

'He got a job on the railway when he came out of jail,' he replied in a loud whisper, which caused Miss Morton, the new assistant school teacher sitting in front of us, to turn half round.

The pews filled up just before the service started and over the heads I was only able to see Maisie's hat. I wondered what her sister Jenny was doing. She must be about leaving school, I thought.

The sermon was about the Holy Spirit coming at Pentecost and although I listened for a while, the vicar's voice was not one for riveting attention and my eyes, resting on the ancient mortice and tenons in the back of the pew in front of me, led me to ponder on how long ago those old oak joints had been cut and fitted and the sort of man who might have driven in the dowels to pull them tightly together, long before anyone had ever heard of the Kaiser and long before all those men now lying beneath the desecrated soil of

France, had been born. The evening sun came through at that moment and streamed in over the congregation. I could see Maisie's hat, its yellow straw and blue ribbon amidst the old stone pillars. Now the vicar had finished and the organ was leading in for the final hymn. I could see the sunbeams pouring in shafts from the high leaded windows above the Norman arches. Undisturbed, delicate cobwebs hung in unreachable corners. I wondered how many miles, as the crow flies, it was to a certain stone church in Flanders with its tower shelled to pieces. I had walked round the fragments of its single bell that lay with its frayed rope entwined with the chestnut trees in the churchyard, and we had used its altar rail to lever away the strewn upturned gravestones to clear a pathway for our ambulances to bring in the dying for shelter in what remained of the nave and vestry. I struggled to reconcile my memories while I regarded the backs of people singing and the dust sparkling round the cobwebs in the golden, hopeful sunbeams. I could see Colonel Lester sitting in the front row with his two daughters and son. He had been at Gallipoli and in France: did he wonder what had been achieved by the sacrifice of the many grieving families throughout the land?

We closed our hymn books and, after the vicar had followed the little choir back to the vestry, smiled round at each other.

When we filed out Maisie and her aunt were well behind Simon and myself. I was apprehensive about meeting her as our last encounter had not been pleasant. Also, I had been avoiding the vicar lately as he had been very quick to ask me to ring the church bell again, regularly one Sunday in the month. I had not given an immediate answer and now, as I neared the door where he was conversing with departing parishioners, I could see he had his eye on me.

'Ah, my dear Abey! May we count upon you from the second Sunday next month?' he beamed as I neared him.

'Yes, Vicar. All right,' I answered.

'We're looking for strong young men to dig that patch over under the east wall. It's become very unsightly and the PCC want the weeds digging out so we can seed it.'

I tried to think of a reason for not being able to do it but failed. 'I'm working quite late some evenings,' I said, expecting what came next.

'Ah yes, of course; but any evening or perhaps Saturday afternoon might be possible. Might it not?'

'Well, I expect so,' I said.

'Splendid!—Let me know in the next couple of days when to expect you, or I'll call in at Hardwick's and see what you've planned.' Then, on seeing Simon waiting just ahead of me, he called 'Don't forget the pruning,

Thursday evening, Simon!'

I turned to leave the church and found myself next to Maisie Hawtin who, with her aunt, had bypassed me and the vicar. She smiled and I, finding myself so near to her suddenly, was unable to think of anything to say.

'Hello Abey!' she said.

'Hello!'

'I'm glad you're back safely.'

'Oh yes; well, oh yes; thanks,' I mumbled.

Her aunt said 'You haven't been to see me yet, Abey. I want you to look at one of my chairs. It needs a bit of something doing to it.'

They walked on and Simon and I followed Bunker and Mrs Cobham towards the gate.

The workshop was busy with local work. Mr Hardwick never turned down a job, whatever it might be. The days of exclusive wheelwrighting had gone before my time and although we still built waggons and carts right through the 1920s, we also covered an increasingly wide range of carpentry work. As the years passed so the emphasis changed, with less wheel and waggon work to more general woodworking including a little furniture making. Ben James, who was now eighty and finding the rigours of the workshop increasingly difficult to cope with, had decided to retire from regular working. He was a fine craftsman in one of the most exacting of handcrafts and would be sorely missed in the wheel work, although more and more factories were advertising ready-made wheels with tyres fitted and axles of every sort and size. The other men, and there were some among them with excellent skills, sensed in the going of Ben another milestone in the history of wheelwrighting. He had provided a pillar of ability and experience to which any problem regarding timber or its products could be taken. His method was slow and deliberate. He never hurried and his work was as near perfection as mortal man could make it. He was angered by the encroachment of new materials which, although promising a quicker method, would not produce as long lasting a result. Sadly, the days when a farmer or tradesman wanted a vehicle to endure the conditions of countryside roads, tracks and fields and also to outlast his own lifetime were changing. The coming of the tractor demanded a different vehicle. In Nether Oldston, as in most villages in England, the change seemed very slow to younger men like myself and the faster moving equipment seemed understandably more desirable. Towns and city streets were filling with iron-wheeled motor-cars, vans and lorries, and although horses and waggons were still there, their carriages and carts were acquiring iron wheels with the hard, solid rubber tyres I had seen on army vehicles. As the country roads improved, so the heavier metal wheels became more popular for the horse-drawn vehicles that plied between local town and outlying villages. Deeper rural conditions, with their thick mud or hard dry ruts sometimes up to the axles in depth, still needed the big wooden wheels which had stood the test of time; here, speed and time were of secondary importance to the decision whether a team of horses could move a waggon in prevailing conditions.

During my earlier training as a wheelwright I had absorbed the pride and delight of the skilled man in his material. To me, even at my age and with only a few years experience, wood had become a revered material. The more I handled it and fashioned it and the more familiar I became with its structure and character, the more convinced I was that for certain work it was the perfect material. I sometimes pondered on its provision, from acorn or seed of the different species, and on the reliability in different ways of the timber of each species. Real skill involved a feeling for, and understanding of, this material. To remain partly in awesome wonder of timber while working it helped one to select and fashion it so that it provided all that could be asked of it. I delighted in the use to the full of what God had provided. How much more would old Ben, who had handled countless trees: ash, oak, elm and beech, of every shape and quality, for nearly seventy years. How impossible for him to come to terms with the declining requirement for the standards once demanded.

The fashioning of wheels and waggons from local trees was not just a matter of learning how to do it, and it was Ben who had taught me awareness of the other factors involved. So many hours were spent at it that it became a way of life. What else one contemplated and did was done in harmony with the workshop life and its background. There was so much more to it than I had envisaged when I was first attracted to a life of working wood. Learning from Ben, I had absorbed some of his sadness, frustration, indeed impatience at the general ignorance of the properties and glories of this living material, which was grown from the English soil, as our generation responded to the results of the war in manufacturing progress and turned away from the satisfaction of hand working.

*　　　*　　　*

Towards the Christmas of my first year back we had glass put in the windows of the workshop. It was a big improvement, for the bitterness of winter was often hard to bear when working, even if the weather was not at its worst. If the wind blew icily and the snow came, it was cruel to endure. Sacking had to be hung up to keep the worst weather from blowing in and sometimes it became quite impossible to do any fine work. In any case, work dropped off during winter-time and tasks such as sawing and moving timber, the sorting and stacking of stocks and planks were gladly accepted, although one's feet were always cold, even if some sort of glow could be generated from exertion.

Another pleasant task was to work in someone's house doing carpentry, so it was with eager anticipation that Jes set off for Briers Nook, next to 'poor old Sloan Carter', where Mrs Maycock lived.

CHAPTER TEN

Uncertainty grew in me. The first months back were like being on long leave. The wartime background, with all its horror, in some strange way had afforded security. The way of life, the day-to-day existence, the mobility of relationships, the wisdom of never looking into matters of importance, with its 'here today and gone tomorrow' philosophy, were hammered remorselessly into the young soldier.

The habit of longing for home, for the war to end, the dreaming of England and living there when it was all over had created a fantasy that was hard, even impossible, to fulfil. For a young man, life back in the country, living at Mrs Pickvance's with regular food and baths, the importance of making a good waggon wheel and talking about a good potato crop was like fine wine at first. There was a way in which its purity was like a beautiful morning where one could breathe it in and stand in awe of its simple flavour. But senses soon dull and even the most unlikely things, if perpetuated, become accepted as routine. The spicy excitement, fear, hope, longing, shouting, times of rest, times of fearful activity, the close involvement with death, blood and stench, the love of life in all its aspects, down to the ecstasy of a pair of clean socks, had continuously battered and distorted my senses, leaving them overstretched yet craving for more, as after the administration and then withdrawal of a powerful drug. It was like being taken up by a whirlwind and suddenly put down again. Now I was conscious of being older and my patience was poor.

There were all sorts of events and arrangements made in Remsditch for ex-servicemen and at first people tended to regard me with a sort of benevolence but as time passed it became difficult and indeed sensible to avoid talking about the war. Mrs Pickvance was one of the few I felt able to confide in occasionally. She had lost a much-loved brother in the Boer War. I took to walking on my own or occasionally with Perce Chennel, who had returned soon after me, from the Oxford and Bucks Light Infantry, with severe bronchial difficulties from gas poisoning.

Early one morning I was surprised to find Perce waiting for me when I stepped outside to set off for the workshop.

'Dawsons have laid me off, Abey,' he said, as he began walking along with me.

'I thought they were taking men on,' I said.

'So they were, until a couple of months ago. 'Tis different now. Trade's dropped off and ones like me who don't breathe so good might become a liability. They paid fifteen of us off on Friday.'

'What are you going to do?' I asked him.

He was quiet for a moment, then said 'I wondered if Albert Hardwick might take me on.'

Perce had worked at Trows Farm after leaving school at twelve but had then gone to work at Dawsons in Remsditch, making small tools, for two years before going into the army. Seth Mottram, in spite of his successful horse breeding, was feeling the beginning of the agricultural depression and would not have him back.

I did not feel his chances with Albert were good. 'No harm in asking, Perce, but I don't think he's wanting anyone at the moment. Ben James is retiring in a couple of months but Albert says he's not making up the numbers. We've got a bit of carpentry and the coffin work but the motor-car needs iron wheels and that's the thing that's on the increase. Get into motors if you can, Perce. I've been thinking about it, but my pay will increase when Ben goes.'

'I can only get as far as Remsditch on my bike, Abey. I've got a few pounds from my gratuity and wonder if I should blow it on a motor bike. I'd like that but our Mum says 'tis no good without somewhere to go on it.'

Albert had opened the shop and Perce went into his office to find out the prospects. He was not there long. Before most of the men had arrived he came out, looking glum. He shook his head at me, although he went out through the back door to the yard. Albert had only been able to give him one day's work turning the muck stack in the bottom corner of the field.

By the end of 1920 the countryside began to reflect the failure of the promise of a 'land fit for heroes' as agricuture settled into deep depression, markets abroad having been lost during the war and high estate duty afterwards causing increases in tenant farmers' rents. Many farms and estates were sold, for often there was no one left to inherit them. Many ex-soldiers moved into the country to try to make a living from the land they had fought for and dreamed of, but conditions were not encouraging.

Mrs Pickvance had taken on a new puppy. About three months old it was, cross-bred from a cross-bred mother and named Flossie. I started taking her on my walks across the fields, having made her a collar from a piece of old harness, to which I tied a length of string until we were clear of the village. As soon as she saw the piece of string she would become a bundle of quivering energy, jumping up into the air, making it difficult to get the string tied on. Any slight delay after this point and she would continue to jump and whimper until we set off.

One Sunday after dinner I was half way along the street when Perce Chennel pulled up alongside me on a new motorbike. When he pushed his goggles up I saw that he looked flushed and bright eyed.

'Bought her yesterday,' he said. 'I can get twenty out of her and she cost me £9.8s.6d.' He rubbed the gleaming petrol tank where the two-stroke mixture had left a slight deposit of oil around the filler cap. 'I decided to get one and go and look for work a bit further,' he added cheerily. 'I've heard of a place near Woodstock where they are making motor accessories. I'm going to have a look tomorrow.' He adjusted his goggles, turned up the throttle, let out the clutch and was away.

Beyond Froglies Bridge I let Flossie off the string. She went off like a rocket and returned panting and covered in mud.

'Mrs Pickvance will be pleased,' I murmured as she tried to shake herself over me.

I walked on up the gentle rise on the far side of the bridge and counted Farmer Lane's bullocks. Twenty-one I made it from over the gate. When they saw Flossie one or two of them came towards us so we moved on, as cattle can get silly over a young excitable dog. We stood under an elm to avoid a sudden shower, then turned back to the village.

Ben Steel was digging near his wall. 'Tell Mrs Pickvance to keep that puppy in!' he called.

I waved and nodded but he came towards me.

'I reckon I seed it round my 'en 'ouse two nights ago,' he said.

I shook my head. 'I don't think so, Ben. She's very careful with it.'

'Ah, so she may be, but a young dog like that needs a lot of watching to keep it out of mischief!'

Flossie was by now back on the piece of string and straining it taut while she watched two cats on a wall further on.

Ben started back towards his digging. 'Doctor's bin out to Horace this morning,' he said.

I looked questioningly at him.

'Ah, 'tis 'is breathin',' he said over his shoulder as he walked away. 'Jenny's over there 'elpin' with 'im. She says 'ee won't last. I dunno though, 'ee's been bad before. 'Ee's not as old as me.'

We proceeded on our way and when we reached the place where the cats had been sitting Flossie walked on her back legs, pulling against the string. There was no sign of them now.

Mrs Pickvance was far from pleased when she saw the state of Flossie and put her straight into the shed. 'She can stay in there until you've bathed her, Abey!' she said firmly, muttering something about 'crime and punishment' to the dog as she closed the door on the luckless creature.

The following morning I received a letter from the French Embassy, saying that I had been awarded the 'Medaille d'Honneur avec Glaives' in bronze for services to France during the war.

I showed it to Mrs Pickvance, who threw her arms round me and said 'I should think so too! So they should!'

We were given orders for two new waggons later that week but I could tell that Albert was worried about work in general. I thought we seemed to have plenty, although the sale of milk and eggs had dropped off due to Lane's producing more and Greg Mottram starting a dairy herd as a reaction to declining prices for arable products. Although the number of motor vehicles increased steadily after the war it was not really noticeable in Nether Oldston yet. Apart from the one at Oldston Manor and Abe Pullen's Austin, both of which had been there before I went to France, there were no others at this stage.

For a long time the days and weeks passed in a monotonous dull way that I found very difficult. All the same things were present as before the war yet somehow I could not settle. I managed to do just about what was expected of me and I told myself it was bound to take time, but as the winter of 1920–'21 began to show glimpses of spring I seriously wondered if I was ever going to settle down again. Instead of less and less, I found myself more and more seeing the wild daisies and bluebells in the trenches. The early morning sunrise with small clouds reminded me of the gunfire drifting over the scene when I had scrambled back over muddy shell-holes at dawn, dragging and carrying in the wounded. But the adrenalin was missing. Perhaps I should seek a completely new life somewhere else. I needed to talk things over with someone.

Mrs Pickvance was aware of my growing restlessness and the inclination to talk freely with her was considerable, although I knew that anything I said might reach Albert Hardwick's ears, and he was already showing impatience with my behaviour.

'Get yourself a nice sweetheart, Abey,' Mrs Pickvance would say. 'Don't you see anything of Maisie now? She's a really nice girl. They say the school's lucky to have her there. She'll make somebody a good wife. There's young

119

Sally Pullen too. She needs a good man now that lad of 'ers is growin' up. Nancy says that boy from Remsditch what was 'is father got killed.'

I decided to tell Albert I needed to go home for a day or two.

He was not pleased. 'We've got a lot on Abey, now, with all the spring work coming in. What do you need to go for?—No trouble is there?—I can't pay you unless you're here!'

'No, not really,' I hedged. 'Something's come up that I need to sort out. I won't be more than a couple of days or so.'

He looked hard at me for a few seconds then shrugged. 'I shall expect you back by Friday!' he said and went into his office.

I felt sorry for him. Things were not going well for him: bigger work was slackening and the motor-car was affecting his hopes for the future.

After a week at home spent in aimless indecision I received a letter from Albert Hardwick. Short and straight to the point, it read 'Dear Abey, I cannot afford to have my staff absent indefinitely. Please return at once or I will have to fill your place in the workshop.'

The farmhouse was empty. My father had left to attend to the spring drilling of wheat, my brothers were all about their business on the farm and my mother had gone with the pony to market. After reading the note I sat and stared over the breakfast table at the far wall for some minutes before getting up and calling old Curate, the only dog that had not accompanied the men. I put on my coat and set off along the village to walk and think yet again.

As I approached the village wheelwright's shop I crossed the road for I did not wish to talk to Jimmy Townsend's father about what I was doing. I had been a close friend of Jimmy's when we were at the village school together. His father was the wheelwright and it was in his shop that I had first become interested in the work.

'Morning, Squire Staughton!' called a voice from an upstairs window. It was Jimmy. He had spotted me and was calling across the road. 'Wait there a minute. I'm coming down.'

I wanted to walk alone, and wished I had gone in the other direction or along the fields behind the house.

'How are you then, Abey?' asked Jimmy, slapping me on the arm enthusiastically.

I smiled. 'All right, Jimmy. How are you?'

'Where are you going? Come in for a minute. I heard you were at home. Not got the sack have you?'

I shook my head.

'Not yet. I was just taking the dog for a walk.'

'I'll put my boots on and come with you,' he said.

121

My heart sank. I wanted to think and be quiet. 'It's hardly worth it, Jimmy. I'm only going up round the turn and back along round the fields to the farm.'

'Doesn't matter. Hold on there. I'll only be a minute. Come in the shop and say hello to Dad.'

Mr Townsend was helping move a dung cart to one side of the workshop. 'Hello, Abraham. Good to see you!' he said, stopping to re-tie his apron. 'We heard you were about again. What are you doing here, then?'

'Just having a few days off,' I said weakly. I could feel him looking hard at me. People like us did not have a 'few days off' for nothing.

'Ah ha,' he said. 'Well, 'tis a different world coming up now. We're in for a lot of changes, I reckon.'

Jimmy appeared, wearing his boots, and we set off.

'Have you got plenty of work?' I asked.

'They seem to have in the shop,' he said. 'I'm only here for the weekend. I'm up in London now.'

'Doing what?' I asked.

'I'm at The Central School.' He waited for my reaction.

'What's that?'

'Why, The Central School of Arts and Crafts. It's a place for studying handicraft, wood carving, lettering, smithing, pottery. It's a fantastic place. You'd like it, all right.'

122

My reaction was small. 'Oh,' I said.

As we walked out of the village and along the road he looked at me. 'You're very quiet, Abey. Are you all right?'

'Yes.'

We walked on with old Curate plodding along behind us. He was too old to run and chase but loved to savour the variety of scents along the roadside, occasionally stopping to sniff deeply at some extra treat hidden in the grass.

Eventually I asked 'How long are you going to this school place?'

Jimmy ignored the question. 'Is there something on your mind, Abey? You seem sort of different.'

I stared at the road for a few more minutes then snapped ' 'Course I'm different! What do you expect?' I gave a hollow laugh.

We turned away from the road to follow the old bridle path round and across neighbouring farmland. The sun came out brightly for a few moments from behind fluffy white clouds and a big hare shot out in front of us to zig-zag and jump away over a field of winter corn. Curate did not see it but caught the scent and, giving a squeak, set off to chase it for a few yards, then looked back at us as if to say 'It's no good, I'm much too old,' waiting for us to catch up with him.

'That's why I'm going to London,' said Jimmy. 'We're all different, Abey, but things are changing fast as well. You might as well accept it.'

'How can I accept differences when I'm expected to settle back into an unchanged rut as if nothing has happened?' I asked, irritated by his complacent manner and releasing a little of my pent up feelings.

'That's just it.' Jimmy stopped to enlarge his point. 'The rut, as you call it, is going to change. Slowly, perhaps, but it's already beginning if you look closely. Don't try to fit back into it. Be ahead of it! The old wheelwright's trade's going out. Sad, yes. My family's trade for generations. Beautiful skills and abilities, a way of life if you like, but motor-cars, buses and lorries don't want wooden wheels! Come on Abey, wake up! Don't let it all leave you behind. It'll be enough to keep men like my father in business but it won't do for you and me. That's why I'm interested in developing ideas for real craftsmen to follow. Put your skills into something up and coming. We've got a man at The Central School who talks about "fitness for purpose" in furniture making. The new concept of design is exciting, Abey. Get into it and see where you can best develop!'

I was quiet for a few minutes, then asked how he had found all this out.

'Oh, some Johnny I met when I was waiting to be demobbed gave me a magazine to look at and there was an article saying something

124

about it. I was interested and wrote for some information. Come and see The Central School. It's a really good place.'

For a while I remained silent. I could see there was some reality in what Jimmy was saying. I had been aware of being unsettled about the future of the wheelwright's trade when I had first seen the heavy iron and steel wheels on vehicles in France. Albert Hardwick's problems and my depression were connected with this.

'There's no way I could change course at the moment,' I said. 'It's true my apprenticeship is over and I'm considered a skilled man. I've always hoped to have a shop of my own one day, perhaps even take over Hardwick's at the right time. I can't up and off. What would I live on?—Anyway I still love the trade and its woodworking skills. It's me that's the trouble. I'm too confused, too unsettled. I don't fit back in.'

'Look Abey, the whole world's confused, unsettled. People are weary of devastation and death. They want dancing, light, beautiful things. Look at the trouble and care that's been put into memorials all over the country. We've had committee meetings, talked to architects, looked at lettering designs. Men like Eric Gill and Edwin Lutyens are talked about. People want a finer, more worthy world for the sake of their loved ones who died. Anyway, the wheelwright's work is going to change and you want to be in there changing it, not dragging along with the inevitable, resenting it and thinking it's a pity.—Did you see that motor over in the corner of our shop here? Dad's putting the carriage work on it for a baker in town. He's got two more coming in. There's going to be plenty to do for those ready to do it. You're a skilled man. Adapt yourself and lead the way. Get interested! It's exciting, I think. You should see some of the design work up at the school!—Look, why don't you come up and let me show you round? I'm going back tomorrow. Come with me and have a look!'

I had Mr Hardwick's letter in my pocket and was already planning to return to Nether Oldston tomorrow. I looked across the farmland. We climbed a stile to follow along the headland where a team of horses was harrowing farther down the field. The scene was unchanged since many years before the war. We walked on in silence with old Curate behind us snuffling along over the fresh, richly scented seedbed earth.

'What will you do when you've finished at this school?' I asked.

'I'm not sure yet; but are you going to come and have a look?'

The horse team was approaching us and as it turned with a jingle of harness I caught the tang of earth and horse-sweat and oiled metal. 'The trenches! The aid post, the mud!' I

126

thought.

'Time I got back, Jimmy,' I said. 'I've got a few things to do and I must get back to Hardwick's tomorrow.'

We turned to cross the corner of the field and headed back towards the village.

CHAPTER ELEVEN

The carrier took me from Remsditch to The Green at Nether Oldston next day.

Mrs Pickvance met me at her door with an anxious face. As I carried my bag indoors she said 'Albert wondered if you were going to come back. I told him he expects too much.— How are you now, then? Have you sorted things out?'

'I will do,' I said. 'I need a bit of time.— Where's Flossie?'

At this she looked startled. 'Oh my goodness, where is she!?'

She called in the kitchen and upstairs, then outside in the back garden.

'She's gone! Little beggar! She must have slipped out when I looked to see if you were with the carrier.'

Leaving my things in the kitchen, I got the old bike out of the shed. 'She's most likely gone by the allotments and up the hill,' I said while pumping a little more air into the tyres.

127

'See if she's gone over to the farm while I go up the hill.'

'Little varmint! She's like an arrow! Wait till I get hold of her!' shouted Mrs Pickvance, taking her broom and setting off.

I pedalled hard, calling and whistling at likely points, but no Flossie appeared. I suddenly thought of Wilbur Gathercole's hens. Flossie was always very attracted by chickens and their fluttering wings. I caught a glimpse of her as I pedalled towards the slope behind the Gathercole buildings where some young pullets were folded in grazing units. I could hear the squawking as I left the bike by the hedge and ran over towards her, shouting 'Come here, Flossie. Come here!'

Looking round in surprise, she made as if to run off.

'Flossie, come here!' I ordered. 'Flossie!'

She froze and her tail went down. She crawled towards me, dragging her rear end, then lay down until I reached her.

Picking her up, I slapped her back-side, saying firmly and breathlessly 'Bad dog!'

While she had sniffed and run round them, the pullets had all huddled into one corner of the wire run, safe but alarmed. She had not been there long, but out of the corner of my eye I could see Wilbur making his way up from the bottom corner of the field.

He was carrying his gun and half running, shouting as he came nearer. 'Put that dog

128

down! I'm goin' to shoot it!'

I waited until he reached me.

Breathless and angry he went on, 'What are you doin' up here interfering on my land? That dog was attacking my pullets! Spoil 'em that will. It needs shootin'! Nothin's safe from a dog like that. Put it down and let me do it!'

'Come on, Wilbur! I got here as quick as the dog. It's only a puppy! Your pullets get more ruffled by the fox than this. I'll see it doesn't come up again. It's Mrs Pickvance's puppy and she doesn't normally take her eye off it.'

'I don't care whose puppy it is! Set them pullets right back, it will; might put 'em right off lay. Put it down and let me finish it off!'

I shook my head. 'It won't come up here again, Wilbur.'

I walked back to where I had left my bicycle by the hedge.

He called after me. 'Interfering young busybody you be gettin'! I'll shoot you as well if you gets between me and that dog next time!'

I cycled back with the dog under one arm and put her in the kitchen.

I saw Mrs Pickvance heading back towards me. 'Don't be too hard on her,' I said; 'I've told her off. How about a nice cup of tea before I go to see Albert?'

Ruffled and hot, she strode past me and went to shout at poor Flossie. Her broom caught a china pot with a geranium as she went through the hallway. It crashed to the ground, leaving an array of blue and white pieces amongst the scattered soil around the suddenly exposed root.

I put the kettle on and took my bag upstairs, then after a quick change of clothes went down to drink the tea that Mrs Pickvance had made. She was still red faced, but the broom had gone back behind the front door and Flossie was in her basket with only her eyes moving.

'You tell Albert what's what, Young Abey. Tell him you've a life to live as well as him!'

I nodded.

As I left she added 'I need some sticks for the fire tonight.'

Only Harry Teemer spoke as I entered the workshop. 'Afternoon Abey. Had a good holiday then?'

I nodded, ignoring the sarcasm. The other men nodded. Although a little uneasy, I was even then aware of the comeliness of the old shop.

Albert was sorting out woodscrews from the big double cupboard at one end of his office. He looked round at me as I entered and raised his eyebrows. 'Hello, Abey; you got back then.—Hold on, while I give these screws to Jes.'

He reappeared quickly. 'There's quite a bit of work piling up since old Ben's gone. George is doing steadily but I want you to get on with the wheels with him. Time o'year's gettin' on.

Ben Steel and Harry are finishing off that muck cart for Langfords. They should be done by next week, apart from painting. They can get on with you as well then. We lost a bit of time with you away last week. I've got some oak coming in on Tuesday if the ground's dried out enough. They've got a tractor up by Jailer's Barrow moving stuff but with the rain they had to pull the tractor out with horses!— Are your folk all right?' he ended.

'Yes; they said to remember them to you.'

'Good. You'll be all right now, then.' There was a trace of anxiety in his voice.

'Yes, fine,' I replied, thinking of what he might say if I suggested a day to look round the school of arts and crafts with Jimmy Townsend.

'We sorted out the fellies and Harry has been truing some of them up, so if you get going with the Crosswood wheels, as soon as he's done on that cart I'll get him to join you.'

'I'll make a start then,' I said and went to begin turning over the pieces of ash that Harry had sorted out.

These had been sawn out roughly to shape and oversize and stacked to allow air to pass between them during a previous winter—it was customary to keep such tasks for cold weather. This final seasoning would eventually produce the fellies, the hard pieces with which to make the outside circle of the wheel, but during this process, they tended to twist a little as they

131

settled and if any defect in structure had previously gone unnoticed it would be revealed now. Over the following months the stacks would have been turned and checked.

As I took the template for the fellies down from the wall and blew the dust off it, Simon Gathercole told me there was a beetle drive at Dagston that night and asked if I was going.

'I might.'

'There was someone asking for you in here last week,' said Simon.

'Oh, and who was that?'

'She asked for your address and when you would be back. She didn't give her name: said her husband had known you in the war. Well dressed woman she was. Came in a motor. Albert was out.'

I wondered who it could have been.

'I've done the hard work for you, Abey!' called Harry Teemer from the nearly finished muck cart. 'Took nearly quarter of an inch off some of 'em.' He came over to look at the ash with me. 'That's the last bit of that stuff he had from round the back of Oldston House. Ah, before the war that was. You won't remember it. Before your time it was. There's still a bit to come off some of 'em,' he added as he turned them over critically. 'We're goin' to take this cart through fer paintin' now so you'll 'ave a bit more room.'

The evenings were getting light now so Simon and I biked up to Broughton Dagston for the beetle drive. It was well attended, and among the many local folk that I knew I spotted Maisie and her sister at a table with Miss Harbottle. During the refreshments interval Maisie introduced me to Mr and Mrs Luker. He was a chartered accountant with a London office. They lived in what was known as The Lodge on the outskirts of Nether Oldston and he was organising the setting up of a memorial for those from Broughton Dagston, Nether Oldston and Lonestock who had been killed in the war. So far, no design had been decided upon. The beetle drive was in aid of this scheme and now, as much discussion had taken place and it was felt that action was needed, he was keen to involve a good architect. He told me that Edwin Lutyens had designed one of the memorials that he had been to see recently. Lutyens was one of the important architects that Jimmy had mentioned and who had been involved in the designing of British war cemeteries in France. Among the names to be put on the local memorial were Jake Pooley, Sammy Blofield, Peter and Fred Auger, and Pip Horner. It was to be set in stone, either at the road junction between Oldston and Dagston, where it was possible to look down across Oldston and also see part of Dagston and over the fields to Lonestock, or as part of the church wall in Nether Oldston, the most central point in the three closely linked communities.

Mr Luker was keen to have the inscription cut by Eric Gill, whose name I again immediately recognised from my talk with Jimmy Townsend. He went on to say that an architect friend of the Purton-Hentises was helping to decide on the position and was preparing drawings for the committee to consider. The Purton-Hentises were still in London for the season until the end of April but Mr Purton-Hentis was in touch about it and had been able to attend meetings. I asked Mr Luker if he knew how Miss Charlotte was and what she was doing. I had not seen her since her time in the army hospital nor heard of her for some months.

He shook his head. 'She's been away since last year. In London I believe. She was injured somehow during the war. Ambulance work or something, I believe.—Why are you asking?'

'Oh, I met her briefly in France. I knew she was wounded and wondered what had happened to her.'

Mrs Maycock interrupted at this point. 'You better make your little speech now, Mr Luker, before we start again,' and led him away to make his appeal for the memorial.

At half past nine one of Will Auger's sons came hurrying in to say his cows were out and heading towards Froglies Bridge. Will and his wife left at once but the playing continued until ten o'clock. Afterwards I left Simon at his house and as I pedalled home past Crosswood

Farm all seemed quiet. When I reached The Green I overtook Will.

'They hadn't gone far,' he said. 'One of them boys it'll be. Didn't put the chain on. I'll 'ave 'im termorrer for it, young beggar!'

'Is that you, Abey?' asked Mrs Pickvance as I closed the door of Number Three behind me.

'Yes,' I said, pushing Flossie down and waiting at the bottom of the stairs.

'Someone was here earlier, asking for you. Came in a big motor, she did. She's staying at the Jersey Arms in Remsditch and coming to see you Friday evening.'

'Who's that, then, I wonder?'

'She didn't say no more. Well-to-do woman, she was. There was someone else in the motor with her, but I couldn't see properly as it was stopped just along a bit and she stood in front of me in the doorway. I walked out to the gate with her but I still couldn't make out much, except there was another person as well as the driver.'

As I lay in bed looking at a small patch of moonlight on the rug by my washstand I wondered again who this woman might be and what she wanted.

Next morning I prepared to turn the two pieces of elm to make the stocks for the Crosswood wheels. Still powered by hand, the big old lathe had to wait for Bertie to finish seeing to the livestock outside before turning could begin. I marked out the centre and chopped off the corners of each block. Albert came over to look at the cleft oak that Bertie had carried in the day before for making into spokes. The oak for spokes was always cleft up in the woods when first sawn and still unseasoned, during winter while the sap was down. It split beautifully then and Albert bought it like that to be stacked and trimmed during the coldest days. Cut approximately to length, these pieces were slowly dried to become the strong, tough as wire pieces needed for spokes.

'When are you going to get a bandsaw, then?' I asked Albert. 'Nobody saws and chops fellies out by hand any more.'

'Can't afford one yet,' he said without looking up.

'It'll be cheaper than paying a man to cut them out by hand—and look now, how I'm held up waiting for someone to turn the lathe. I could have turned those two stocks while I'm waiting for Bertie.'

Albert took off his hat and knocked the dust from it on his knee. 'I don't need tellin' how to run my own business, Abey. Things'll change soon enough without me rushing to help it.'

Bertie went up into the loft to power the lathe. I took the long-handled gouge and began to fashion the first big stock as it rumbled and spun round.

'If an engine was driving this, Bertie could see what I was doing. He won't learn much up

136

in that loft!' I said as Albert went back past me.

He did not look round and appeared not to hear me.

The elm chips flew off as the old lathe chattered until the stock became centred and sent out streaming shavings. Different wheels had different shaped stocks. Quickly the traditional farm cart shape with its bullnose appeared. As the timber spun round, the recesses for the iron bonds, or bands, of iron, which would be fitted next door at the blacksmith's, were cut and two light lines inscribed to mark for morticing the spokes, which would be done after I had matched the second stock to the first. Many shops had the iron bands put on at this stage but Albert preferred to have them fitted at the same time as the iron tyre, although it is true that occasionally these centre bands could be loosened slightly by the extreme compressing force exerted when the red hot tyre was cooled and shrunk onto the wheel.

Bertie reappeared, and after setting out the mortices with dividers we fixed the first stock into the special wooden horse ready for chopping them out. He put my canvas roll of small files on the bench and I touched up the edges of the auger bit before fitting it into the brace. It was usual to remove the main waste from each mortice with the brace and bit. The hard, seasoned, interlocked grain of the elm

137

resisted this with all its might and to bore these holes required considerable strength and stamina. I was glad to let Bertie have a go while I checked him for accuracy but after a few minutes I was interrupted.

'Take Magnolia up to Crosswood, Bertie, and fetch some chaff for the henhouse. See Alan Bourton,' Albert called.

I looked out at the blue sky, aware of the contrariness of human nature within myself: I envied Bertie going off with the cart while I proceeded to do what in the past I had complained of not being allowed to do. I continued to strive with the brace and bit. In the past I had often watched the sweat pour from Ben's face when boring out the elm.

*   *   *

Horace was not improving and I called to see him after work. His wife was out so I let myself in.

His coughing was very bad and he could not talk. As I sat by his bedside he pointed to the chair I was sitting on and smiled. It was one of the walnut ones that I had helped him make before the war. I told him about Jimmy Townsend and how I was becoming more interested in the design of furniture making. He nodded while he listened with his eyes closed. I felt Horace would have been interested to see what was going on at The

138

Central School in London, although it was said that he had never been farther than Remsditch and only there three times in his life. There was nothing I could do so after a little while, before leaving, I plumped up his pillows and cushions and then laid my hand on his shoulder for a minute. He smiled without opening his eyes.

Outside the pigeons were calling to each other and the spring sunshine was casting its lengthening shadows across the quiet village street. From afield up by Froglies Bridge I could hear the faint shouts of young lads making the most of the longer daylight hours, playing football.

Two days later I had a note from Jimmy Townsend. A magazine was enclosed with an article about The Central School.

The talk I had had with him had set me thinking. I could see that there was a danger of Hardwick's not keeping up with the times and that maybe I should seriously consider changing course. Still unsettled, I found my interest and concentration difficult to maintain. I knew this was a common problem in the aftermath of war—but did I want to be a wheelwright in the changing new world that was moving fast from carts and horses to motor-cars, and where the machine was superceding the hand?

I lit the oil lamp in my bedroom after supper and read the article. It described how the art school was looking ahead, with its ideas and plans for training artists and craftsmen to influence and create the new world. Metal, stone, weaving, tapestry, painting and woodwork were all mentioned. 'The true craftsman must understand the nature of his material', I read. A photograph of a rush-seated chair by Ernest Gimson was shown and a piece of Roman lettering from a recent memorial by Eric Gill. Jimmy had mentioned both these names and I had begun to think much about them. Perhaps I could get some books about all this. I wrote back to Jimmy asking if any were available and wondered if I might somehow, after all, go up to see what was happening at this art school.

The next evening I went up to Broughton Dagston to see Mr Luker and to ask him what form the village memorial was going to take and if the inscription had been decided upon. I showed him the bit about the letter-cutting in the magazine article and he expressed interest. He suggested I might like to go with him to look round the school and seek their advice about the memorial before he met the architect.

When I arrived back at Number Three, Mrs Pickvance was wearing her best skirt. She had been that evening to the inaugural meeting of the Women's Institute.

Quite excited she was, and wanted to tell me all about it. 'Lovely, it was, Abey! There was daffodils everywhere and I've never seen the school look so nice! Crowded, too. Everyone was there. Women that is, of course; even old Daisy from the shop and old Meg Mottram. That Mrs Maycock was there of course. She doesn't miss anything and always got plenty to say. They asked her to thank Lady Esterdale for coming and opening it. Even Mrs Purton-Hentis had come down from London to be there. We've never had such a do here before. Mrs Tringham from up at Dagston is our first President. We're going to be busy making things and going to lectures regularly like. Pity you men haven't got anything like that. I wonder you don't start something instead of wastin' your time in pubs and playin' games!'

It was later than usual by the time she had quietened down and fed Flossie and we got to bed.

After I had turned out my lamp I heard her calling out of her door: 'Don't forget that smart woman's comin' to see you tomorrow night! You better get back in good time. I shall have to ask her in.'

*   *   *

Next day I began chopping out the mortices in the wheelstocks where I had bored holes to remove some of the waste. It was customary to build a wheel from the centre outwards. First the stock, then the spokes made and fitted,

141

then the fellies. As I worked I thought back to the big heavy iron-and-wood wheels on the gun carriages. I saw the mud and horses knee-deep in it, struggling with sliding gun carriages, and men shouting.

'You be dreamin' agin, Abey!' said Harry, who had joined me to work on the wheels.

I started.

'You missed one of they mortices yesterday, I see,' he said, turning over the other stock on the bench and pointing to it.

I shrugged and we set it up for him to do.

The mortices were finished by chopping out the remaining waste with a tool called a registered chisel. This was not quite as hefty as a mortice chisel but heavier and stronger than the normal 'firmer' type. It had an iron ferrule round the top to prevent it splitting from constant striking and a leather washer between its steel shaft and wooden handle to act as a shock absorber. The corners of each mortice were cleaned out square with a special corner chisel called a bruz.

'Horace ain't no better, then,' said Harry, re-tying his apron before starting to turn the brace. 'Fitsy reckoned he wouldn't last another week.' He went on pulling at the brace for a few minutes, then added 'She says 'is boy's a comin' to see 'im tonight.'

Horace had got a son somewhere. I had never seen him and no one seemed to know much about him except that he was in the navy in the war and was something to do with engineering and shipyards.

As I was leaving the shop that evening Albert called me into his office. 'I won't delay you long, Abey, but you might as well know that I'm not ignoring progress. I've already been to look at a possible bandsaw and a hand-morticer. These changes can't be made in minutes; you'll find progress is best made slowly. Timber needs skilled hands to produce the best. A machine might do it quicker but it'll ignore the differences in material and it can't reject an unsuitable piece.—Anyway, I thought you might like to know we're getting another engine, as well, with a countershaft that'll take the power to a bandsaw and the lathe.'

I was pleased, and nodded in approval. I thought it might be a good moment to mention a possible visit to London and the art school, but he went on 'Gordon Luker tells me he wants to take you up to London to see about a design for the war memorial.' He frowned at me.

'Well, yes. He mentioned the possibility. I was going to see what you thought about it.'

He went on frowning. 'We're behind here with the work now. You've already been away for best part of a week. What is it you need to see up there?'

I decided to throw caution to the winds.

'Things are changing very fast, Mr

143

Hardwick, and from what I've seen and heard there's a big new interest in designing things for our post-war age.'

Albert began to knock more dust from his hat and started sneezing. He held up his hand.

In between sneezes he tried to say something, but I went on. 'The motor-car and its engine, the men who have come back, more people with more money are all making a difference. I need to see what's going on.'

'Rubbish!' he said louder than usual. 'There's always folks who'll want to stir up trouble and cause unrest. You'll find plenty of Blackshirts and the like up in London. Young folks like you take it all in. I've seen it all before. Those who keep their heads and go on quietly weather the changes best!'

'Well, I can't go if you won't give me the time off!' I said as we glared at each other.

He jammed his hat back on. 'You'll have to make the time up on Saturday afternoon and evenings!'

He walked past me and out of the office. I followed him and collected my dinner bag.

He waited at the big doors to lock up. 'Tell me as soon as you know which day you are going,' he said as I went out.

We walked together as far as his house in silence where he said 'Good-day, Abey,' and I answered 'Good-day, Mr Hardwick.'

*   *   *

It was only as I neared Number Three and saw the big Rolls Royce that I remembered I was having a visitor. Mrs Pickvance had told me to be early and now here I was late and still in my working clothes!

The door of the front parlour was open when I entered and Mrs Pickvance said 'Here he is at last.—Where have you been Abraham? You'll have to come in like that now. You can't keep these ladies waiting any longer!'

The two ladies stood up to greet me. 'How do you do, Abraham,' said the elder one and held out her hand. 'I'm Mrs Jackson, Captain Jackson's mother. I believe you were associated with my son in France during the war. This is René Shawcross, to whom he was engaged to be married.'

I shook hands with them both and they sat down again, among Mrs Pickvance's best cups full of tea. She poured me one, spread a small dust sheet over the chair seat where I was to sit to protect it from the sawdust in my trousers and went out, closing the door firmly behind her.

'I apologise for having arrived at an obviously inconvenient time,' began Mrs Jackson.

I shook my head as she went on. 'But we so wanted to meet you and talk to you just for a few minutes. I believe you were with my son when he died. You wrote to my husband and

145

sent his personal belongings. We wanted to thank you personally.'

I nodded and half smiled. Miss Shawcross, who was weeping quietly, tried to smile too.

'My husband would have come but he collapsed soon after hearing of my son's death and never recovered.'

She fumbled in her handbag and took out a small box. 'We thought you might like to see this,' she said, handing it to me as she opened it.

I looked at the Military Cross in silence then closed the box and handed it back to her with a nod.

We sat quietly for a few moments and sipped the tea. Then, I related as much as I could of what I remembered of the captain and his work in the aid post. It was a very sad little meeting there in the parlour with the evening sun going down outside and the sound of a cuckoo, insisting on the hopes of spring even in the fading of another day.

It was difficult to know exactly what to say yet I sensed these ladies were seeking anything at all to feed their memories and fill the unbearable gap in their lives. I heard of the captain's academic brilliance: school on an organ scholarship, a double first at Durham University, medical school and organist at the city cathedral. He would have been twenty-nine on his birthday last Wednesday.

As the light faded to a point when I said I

would light the lamp, Mrs Jackson said they must not keep the driver waiting any longer.

She gave me her address and said to her companion 'Come along René dear, we must go,' then to me, 'Do thank Mrs Pickvance for us.—I would like to keep in touch with you, Abraham, and don't give another thought to meeting us in your working clothes; in fact I'm glad you did. I need to hold on to the realities of life, and to direct my attention to the wholesomeness of physical toil and the common round. Thank you again for all you did for my son at the end.'

In a few moments they were gone, for when they emerged from Number Three their chauffeur was already turning the starting handle at the front of his gleaming limousine and when he held the door for them to get in the engine was ticking over beautifully.

Mrs Pickvance joined me at the front gate to wave them off, and almost silently they drove away.

'Poor souls,' she said as we went inside, adding 'I gave the driver a cup of tea.'

CHAPTER TWELVE

Harry was needed for a waggon repair near Lonestock soon after we had prepared the spokes for the Crosswood wheels, so I was left to cut the tenons, with their slightly angled shoulders to give a small amount of 'dish' to the wheels. This dish, one of the construction secrets of a strong wheel, was also necessary to throw the turning wheel out from touching the side of the cart at the top. The small angle was checked on each spoke as it was fitted by a simple gauge held in the wooden horse with the stock, the mortices having already been cut to accommodate this.

When ready, the spokes were driven into the stock dead tight with a sledge hammer, then they were marked to length and a tenon or tongue cut on each one to fit into the fellies forming the outside ring.

Bertie joined me later in the day and I instructed him in a little spokeshaving of the fellies while I finished cutting the tongues with a chisel and drawknife. The ash for fellies was always very hard, due to its original selection and rough cutting to shape before seasoning. Spokeshaving was hard on the thumbs especially to the uninitiated. I noticed Bertie flagging once or twice but he persevered very well until he announced, with some relief I suspected, that it was time to return to his stockman role outside.

At the end of the week we heard that Horace had died. As Harry told me the news I glanced across to his bench. His apron was still folded on the top with a layer of dust and a handbrush upon it. His big beech try-plane was just as he had left it some three weeks earlier when he had gone home coughing in the evening air, stopping to collect tobacco from the shop.

'Albert will need to set someone on soon if he's going to keep up with production!' said Harry. 'That's two skilled men gone in six months and nobody to replace them in sight!'

Before nightfall Jes and Albert Groom had sorted out suitable oak for Horace's coffin box.

As they carried the heavy boards to the bench for planing I heard Albert say ' 'Ee would 'ave said flowered oak was a waste.'

'Well, he ain't got no say in it now and his wife won't bother much, that's fer sure. We'll give 'im the best,' Jes replied.

The following Friday Mr Luker called at the shop to say he was going to London and to see if I would be able to go with him. I looked across at Albert who was near enough to hear what was said but he pretended he had not and went on working.

I went to him and asked.

'Yes, all right, but like I said you'll have to come in Saturday afternoon and evenings next week,' he replied, without looking up from what he was doing.

At that moment the vicar looked in at the doorway, calling out that one of Greg Mottram's straw ricks was on fire. Immediately Albert, all the men and Mr Luker left what they were doing and hurried round to the farm

149

rickyard. Smoke was billowing thickly everywhere and Abe Pullen was carrying buckets round to the farm men, who were throwing water round the next rick to prevent the fire from spreading. A ladder was against the burning rick on the windward side and water was being thrown into the smoke. But the fire was gaining rapidly and there were shouts for the men to come down before it was too late. The flames leapt up now and the fire roared and crackled with each gust of wind, driving us all back. The second rick began burning and there was a danger of it spreading to the barns and a hayrick.

A man had already been sent off by bicycle to fetch the fire brigade from Remsditch in case a telephone call from the post office had not got through.

A small firefighting unit, kept up at Crosswood Farm, consisted of a four-man operated water pump with a length of leather hosepipe and a brass nozzle at one end. It was mounted on four wheels and drawn by a single horse. This had now arrived and was ready to start. The intake hose was not long enough to reach to the stream so it had been put in a horse trough and a human chain of buckets was connecting it with the stream. The jet of water was directed at the second rick in the hope of holding the fire back until the brigade arrived. Calves from the nearby barn were being moved out and horses from stables led away wide-eyed and fearful through the swirling smoke and past the burning area. The water pump was emptying the horse trough faster than we were filling it and shouts of 'Faster!' were passed along. More buckets arrived and another chain formed alongside ours. Somebody wondered if the stream was high enough to supply it all. In the distance the fire-engine bell could be heard on the road from Remsditch. The wind changed for a few minutes, causing pandemonium among the firefighters nearer the ricks as the flames leaped round towards them. The fire-engine bell, which could now be heard getting louder and louder, suddenly seemed to stop because the wind had turned for a moment but then its clanging showed that it had entered the village and a few moments later it swept into the farmyard. A cheer went up from the bystanders, who included children from school who had been let out to watch.

The new motor-driven fire-engine was a reassuring sight with its red paint and polished brass and its voluntary crew of eight local tradesmen, still buttoning their blue uniforms, who tumbled out and began laying out their hoses. Their leader (I recognised him as a butcher from Remsditch) quickly assessed the challenge and ordered people from the danger areas. Very quickly the situation was brought under control and although the second rick was almost totally lost the barns and hayrick were saved.

Sally Pullen had brought her little boy Owen to watch. He was now five years old and I could see him tugging at his mother's hand to get nearer the fire-engine.

'I can't keep him out of the shop at home, Abey,' she said. 'It's all right when his grandfather knows he's there but he'll go in there on his own sometimes when I'm not watching and I'm frightened he'll get under one of them horses when they're busy with the shoeing. But anyway now, Abey, I'm glad I've run into you. It's past his birthday but I wondered if you would make him a little wheelbarra. I'll pay you of course. I know you're always busy but he would love one.'

I nodded. 'I'm going up to London Friday and I shall have to make up the time at work next week but I'll see what I can do. He's five now, isn't he? And you haven't found yourself a husband yet, then?'

Sally shook her head. 'No, nor likely to, stuck here in this village, even if all the young men hadn't been killed!'

I began helping to collect the buckets but Albert rounded up his men, saying 'Come on, they can clear up now. There's work waiting for us to do back home!'

*   *   *

When Harry and I finished the wheels for the

Crosswood cart they were taken next door for the blacksmith to put the iron tyres and bonds on.

Albert brought out the old drawings of the dogcart. 'We've got one ordered from right over at Godspur Barret. Man there called Wadley. He saw one of those you made with old Ben. I know he made all the wheels for them but you worked with him. See how you get on. Young Bertie can help you with the cart but get the wheels done first. Keep them nice and fine. We could buy a pair ready made but we've never bought a wheel yet and it'll put you to the test a bit.'

It was over five years since I had made a dogcart with old Ben but I had done a lot of the work on the wheels then. Albert's wife, Gwen, still used the first one that we had made and although Jiffy was that much older now, the pony still trotted smartly around in it. From time to time it came in for the paintwork to be touched up as Albert still regarded it as an advertisement for the shop. I had enjoyed this slightly finer work with Ben and was pleased for the chance to see now what I could do on my own.

Early on Friday morning I was picked up by Mr Luker's motor-car, which took us to Remsditch Railway Station. It started to rain while we waited for the train but right on time the great hissing and steaming engine pulled into the platform. At Paddington Station Mr

Luker hailed a taxi and we went directly to Southampton Row and The Central School of Arts and Crafts. As we walked up the steps to the main entrance I was impressed by how big the building seemed, and I was immediately aware of the wide Arts and Crafts staircase spiralling up to our right. We were introduced to the secretary, a Mr Topping, with whom Mr Luker had corresponded. I told him I had a friend in the school who had urged me to come and look around, so he sent for Jimmy who was attending drawing class.

Mr Luker had other commitments in London after his appointment at the school so while we waited for Jimmy to arrive I arranged to meet him at Paddington for a train home in the afternoon.

'Show Mr Staughton round, let him listen and talk to whom he will, take him to the canteen then bring him back here,' Mr Topping told Jimmy.

Jimmy was delighted I had come and shook my hand enthusiastically.

'We'll start with the Furniture School. You'll like that, and I can show you what I'm working on,' said Jimmy, and he led me along a tall, wide corridor with doors opening into classrooms and workshops.

I felt excited and followed him eagerly.

In the well-equipped workshops I was introduced to Mr Spooner, head of the Furniture School. He was interested to know

154

that I was a wheelwright and asked about the sort of work I was doing. When I expressed my concern about the future of the trade he nodded sympathetically but pointed out that the skills and standards demanded of the wheelwright who had a true understanding of his material were exactly what was being encouraged in his department. He took us to his office to look at photographs of work done by students and explained that the design principles of the School were a natural progression from the influence of John Ruskin and William Morris, then in particular the work of Ernest Gimson, Philip Webb and furniture makers like the Barnsley brothers.

Jimmy led me around the workshops to talk to various students. Most of them were younger men seeking qualifications in future design and making. There were some ex-service men working under a retraining scheme and a few were men of about my age paying privately for their tuition. The work that they were all doing was fascinating and I would have gladly spent much longer looking at it all. There were many interesting ideas being followed and the standard of craftsmanship was wonderful. A dresser being made by one man particularly interested me, so beautiful was the figured oak in relation to the simplicity of the design. A chair almost ready for rush seating also intrigued me with its high back and shaped arms, showing to advantage the grain structure of the wood. Two tools in particular I looked at closely: the steel plane and the coping saw. There had been talk of the former in Hardwick's workshop but this was the first time I had seen or even heard of the coping saw, with its small compact frame and twisting round, fine blades. I handled and liked them both, seeing immediately the usefulness of the saw, but the jack plane that they let me try did not convince me that it would be as comely a tool in general use as the beech plane, although I was aware of its quick adjusting facilities and the fact that when I tried planing with it, my hands were about three inches lower and therefore nearer the surface being worked and thus in more control.

After more looking round at classes, where some very interesting things were going on, including letter-cutting in stone and wood, and the drawing of the Roman alphabet, which directed my attention to the beautiful proportions and balance of each letter with its finely shaped serifs, I resolved there and then to find out more about the Trajan Column, from which the alphabet was taken, and its history, all of which I was made aware of in those few minutes. I felt drawn to the tutor as he talked about these things, linking what we look at and live among with how we are. He quoted William Morris's apparently famous words, which I had never heard before: 'Have nothing in your home which is not beautiful or useful'.

Something within me was stirred as I looked round further, into areas of stained glass and mosaic production, silversmithing and wrought iron, painting and engraving. I was suddenly consciously aware of colour, of form, of involvement with practical beauty. I felt strongly drawn to it, with excitement in my new-felt perception. I could see that these things were all an extension of the wheelwrighting and the blacksmithing in which I was experienced. They were all part of the same history and development of creative working. I could see that the insights of William Morris and John Ruskin could lead us through the heady instability of sudden mass production and its danger of a disregard for beauty and for the importance of a mind at ease. The old crafts were the finest basis on which to develop the new world's requirements!

'Let's have some refreshment,' said Jimmy. 'Are you hungry?'

I nodded and we made our way to the canteen, where students were served with food and snacks.

We sat at a table and tucked into good helpings of Irish stew followed by rice pudding, all of which Jimmy insisted on paying for.

'What do you think of the place?' he asked.

'I'm very impressed,' I said.

'I knew you would be. Apart from the rice pudding, I wouldn't want to change much either.' He went on eating for a few moments, then asked 'What are you going to do about it?'

I finished my helping of Irish stew, lay down my knife and fork, sat back in my chair and said slowly 'I don't know.'

We finished off the pudding and sat with mugs of tea.

'You didn't see my bookcase. I meant to show you. I've just dovetailed the plinth and it's nearly ready to put on. We'll go back and see that before I return you to the office,' said Jimmy.

I did not answer.

He looked hard at me. 'Come on Abey, you can't let it rest now! Decide to come and join me here. Make the decision. Fill in the application form while you are here, now.'

I shook my head. 'I can't, Jimmy.'

'Why not?'

'I can't afford to, and it would leave Albert Hardwick in a hole. Anyway, I'm not sure I want to cut loose from the old shop.'

Jimmy took another swig of tea and remained silent.

I went on 'It's true I'm very attracted to what's going on up here and I'm going back to think things over. I don't intend to just forget all this.'

'You could share digs with me if you can

sort something out,' said Jimmy and I nodded as a possible plan began to form in my mind.

When we reached the secretary's office Mr Topping showed me photographs of previous students' work and said, when I asked him for a copy of the prospectus and an application form, that they would be pleased to consider me if I decided to apply. I thanked him and when I shook hands with Jimmy outside in Theobalds Road we agreed to keep in touch over plans for the future.

At Paddington I joined Mr Luker, who was very pleased with the advice he had had from the School about the memorial inscription, and as the train, amidst great clouds of steam, began pulling slowly out of the station, he was interested to hear about what I had been seeing.

CHAPTER THIRTEEN

During the next few weeks seasonal jobs with farm implements and harvest requirements demanded immediate action and occupied all of our time, delaying progress with the dogcart that I was trying to complete, and the pressure of work kept my mind off my own problems and decisions.

Bertie worked with me most of the time when he was free from tending the livestock and was developing into a useful assistant and one with whom I got on well. I told Albert he was doing well and said he should think about leaving him with me more of the time and perhaps get another lad to start with the stock work.

Albert looked doubtful and shook his head. 'Ah, a bit soon. Don't want to rush him.'

I did not talk to Bertie about my growing interest in furniture design as I felt it might unsettle him with his apprenticeship. The men in the shop would repair a chair occasionally or, using their woodworking skills, if the need arose at home, even make up a piece of furniture, but every one of them was opposed to anything that suggested change in the methods and ways of the wheelwright's and carpenter's shop. Jimmy sent me copies of *The Woodworker* from time to time and newspaper cuttings when relevant to the growing development in furniture making. He sent me his own copy of *Form in Civilization* by W. R. Lethaby, one of the founders and an early principal of The Central School. Articles on the work of some men in the Cotswolds, Peter Waals and the Barnsley brothers, much interested me.

He sent me a copy of *The Studio*, dated October 1919, recording the death of Ernest Gimson and praising his influence on furniture design and making, and suggesting that in years to come his productions would be as eagerly sought after as those of the great cabinet makers of bygone generations. These I read and re-read each evening until I fell asleep, fuelling my growing interest and determination to follow this line somehow. The only person who I felt would have been sympathetic to my interest was Horace, and he had gone. Even the walnut chairs that I had helped him a little with had gone, for his son had taken them away when his widow said there was far too much stuff in the house.

One Friday evening after a day spent up at Hawtin's old yard in Lonestock doing some emergency work on a waggon with Harry, I was pushing my bicycle with him towards the gate when we met Jenny Hawtin, Maisie's younger sister. She asked if I would like to be in a concert that was being planned in the village. Harry went on ahead and I stopped for a moment to ask what she thought I might do.

She said that if I was no good at anything much I could help with the scenery or something. Then she asked 'Still working at Hardwick's, then?—I heard you were on the London train a few weeks ago.—Oh well, nothing changes here much, does it? I'm working up at the House. Like a slave, I am. Do this, do that!—I'll have to stick it till I'm a bit older but I shall have my eye to the main chance and if nothing happens I'll make it happen!—There's the service on Sunday for unveiling the war memorial. We're all coming.

I expect most folk will be there. Tell me then if you think of anything else you could do for the concert.'

She headed for home and I freewheeled down the hill to Nether Oldston. The memorial stone had at last been decided upon and set into the church wall. I pedalled past the Union Jack that would cover it until Sunday and as I passed the closed doors of the workshop, in the quiet deserted evening village, I heard only the soft noise of my bicycle tyres and a thrush singing above the church porch. I was aware of the temporary nature of all things. I felt that a loneliness I had not known before the war was becoming a part of me.

On Sunday morning it was my turn to ring the church bell before the 7.30 Holy Communion service. From my elevated position at the back of the church I could see the assembling congregation, which was larger than usual due to visitors and friends staying locally for the dedication of the war memorial later in the morning. All of the Purton-Hentis family were there including a high-collared, well wrapped-up figure walking with a stick, whom I thought might be Charlotte. I watched her carefully when she went up among the first to receiv communion, for which she remained standing, but with her tightly tied headscarf and high collar I remained uncertain.

Mrs Pickvance had walked home before I

reached there on my bicycle and was cooking breakfast when I arrived.

'Get a move on, Abey. I've got a lot to do this morning. There's tea and biscuits to get ready in the school for the Dagston bandsmen after the service and the Women's Institute have got to assemble in time to march behind the British Legion. Mrs Pinchin and Mary Sanders are calling for me at a quarter to ten!'

Almost everyone from the two villages and Lonestock, plus visitors from Remsditch, gathered in and around the church for the occasion. Chairs were put inside the church but less than half those attending managed to pack in for the service. The band stood outside and played for the hymns and all those outside the church joined in the singing. Afterwards everyone crowded onto the green where Mr Luker, the vicar, the bandmaster and Mrs Maycock ordered the assembling of the procession, which was to march back to the unveiling of the memorial stone in the church wall. There were some anxious glances at the sky, which had clouded over, but apart from a few threatening drops no rain came.

I stood with Perce Chennel, Tim Bourton, Peter Brooks, two daughters of Mr Luker who had been nurses, three ex-servicemen who had come to live in the village since the war and Pearson Grantle's sister, Daphne, who had been with the VAD in France. We all wore our campaign medals. Tim Bourton had a Military

Medal and I my French medal, for which I had received written permission from the King to wear on all occasions when British medals might be worn. Some ex-servicemen from Remsditch also lined up with us. Colonel Lester joined us, the big drum began beating and everyone stood up straight.

'Parade!—By the right—quick march!' shouted a voice, and as the first bars of 'Land of Hope and Glory' sounded the procession moved forward towards the church.

The road was not very wide by the churchyard wall where the memorial had been set, so when the procession reached that point it disintegrated, to re-form around the flag-covered stone where the vicar was waiting in his flowing white surplice. The band went into the churchyard, which was on a higher level than the road, and formed up just above us over the wall. The roadway was crowded in both directions, beyond the school one way, and in the other, past the Bannisters' cottage and even into the lane leading to the back of Hardwick's yard, where the timber waggons went to unload.

The sun remained behind the clouds but quite a large blue patch of sky began to appear above the tall elms at the back of the churchyard, towards Oldston House. Mr and Mrs Purton-Hentis, Colonel Lester and Mr Luker joined the vicar by the flag and the whole assembly fell silent.

164

Mr Luker stepped forward and began the proceedings by drawing attention to the solemnity of the occasion and the pride and hope that we all carried in our hearts, thanking God for all the brave men who had given their lives for our freedom and especially those from our own community whom we knew and loved so well.

Colonel Lester removed the Union Jack. Slowly, and in a loud voice, he read out the names carved in the stone:

'George Henry Auger,
Maurice Bagley,
Samuel Stanley Blofield,
Arthur Tremayne
Pearson Grantle,
Edward John Hawtin,
Philip Horner,
Jacob Ernest Pooley,
Roderick Charles Walker.'

Then the words of Laurence Binyon: 'They shall grow not old as we that are left grow old . . .'

I thought of Sammy's face when Albert sacked him up at Halfroot Farm.

'Age shall not weary them nor the years condemn . . .'

I heard Roderick's voice: 'They say they cut all your hair off when you arrive.'

'We will remember them . . .'

'I would quite like to go,' Pip was saying, 'but I expect it will all be finished before I get there.'

'We will remember them,' repeated the assembly.

A bandsman with a bugle stood high over the wall and sounded 'The Last Post'. In the silence that followed I heard Owen Pullen somewhere behind me telling his mother he needed to do a piddle, and the rooks in the elms still squabbling and sending down a light shower of twigs. The vicar's cockerel crowed, then to end the hush of that gathering of diverse local and visiting folk, standing with bowed heads and sorrowful hearts, the bugler sounded 'Reveille'.

The vicar read a prayer and gave the blessing, gathered up his white raiment and then, after nodding to the people at the front, went back to the church to take his robes off and get a quick tot of medicinal brandy.

The band began Elgar's 'Enigma Variations' and everyone started moving, mostly towards the school where tea was being served.

I could see no sign of Miss Charlotte but her parents were there, both looking old and very frail. I had heard their health was causing problems. They were drinking tea with the vicar and Mr Luker.

Mr Luker made a point of speaking to me. 'The stone looks very well, Abey. I think everyone is pleased with it.—Have you had

166

any further contact with The Central School?'

I shook my head. 'No, I'm afraid not. But I'm still thinking about it.'

'Ah, thinking is all right but not if it is used to avoid action!—I was very impressed with the place and I know you were.'

He turned to Mr Purton-Hentis. 'Abraham and I visited The Central School of Arts and Crafts, you know.'

'Ah yes. Now just where is that?' responded Mr Purton-Hentis, fitting his cup into its saucer. 'Is it London?'

'Yes. Where Southampton Row meets Theobalds Road. A very interesting place. Abraham is thinking about attending one of its courses.'

I looked round, hoping that Albert Hardwick was not within earshot.

'Yes, very good,' said Purton-Hentis and, as someone bumped his elbow in the crowded schoolroom, he almost dropped his cup and saucer.

I took the chance to ask him directly if it was Miss Charlotte I had seen at church.

He looked vague for a moment. 'Er, yes it was. She's home for the weekend, you know.'

'How is she?' I persisted.

'Very well,' he said, looking as if he was surprised that I knew of her existence.

'Come along, dear,' said Mrs Purton-Hentis, 'we must be going now.' She smiled at Mr Luker, removed the cup and saucer from her husband's hand and turned to me. 'Mr Staughton, you must think us dreadfully ungrateful for all you did so bravely for our daughter Charlotte. It's just that we have been poorly, and my husband forgets who people are. Charlotte is recovering, in London, and I'm sure she will contact you when she is well again, to thank you properly.' She gave me a tired little smile before leading her husband away, stopping only to bid farewell to the vicar at the door.

*   *   *

When the dogcart was complete and had received its five coats of goldsize and three of varnish, Bertie was entrusted to deliver it to Mr Wadley at Godspur Barret. He was pleased by this honour but not so happy to learn that he was to walk back afterwards with Jiffy, a distance of about eight miles. Albert said we were too busy to spare another man and cart to bring him back.

The dogcart was something of a triumph for me and for Bertie. It looked good as it stood out in the front of the workshop with Jiffy between its shafts, waiting to go. It was the first item of any consequence that I had completed myself and, under my tuition, Bertie had also been very involved in its construction. I sensed in him an aptitude for the work; his developing skill showed a natural feeling for the material in his hands. His mind, too, was of an inquisitive nature, enjoying the problems of construction, which I found stimulating.

Albert was pleased as we stood outside watching Bertie drive off. He nodded to himself and knocked the dust out of his old hat on the side of a waggon awaiting a minor repair. 'Beautiful!' he murmured. 'You don't see style like that in a dusty, oily, noisy motor-car.'

I felt it was a good time to mention The Central School again. 'A pity there's not the demand for more work like that around here,' I began.

'We've still got plenty of waggon work,' he said.

'I'd like to do some furniture work,' I said, following him towards the open doors of the workshop.

'Oh, ah,' he answered, looking across to Magnolia, who was watching the departure of Jiffy over the field gate.

'Why don't you consider doing a little?' I persisted.

'Wheelwrights and undertakers. That's what we are. That's what my father was, my grandfather, and his father before him. We've had to do more general carpentry in the last years than they would have done, but that's how we're staying. We've got no experience nor demand for furniture work. Harry needs some help with that axle he's doing and when that's done, give George Groom a hand on that big waggon that we've promised for next Wednesday.' He walked inside and went to his office.

I returned to Harry who was adjusting the axle of a dung cart.

Walking home that evening, I pondered on how I might introduce the idea of a part-time course on furniture design. Albert was obviously not inclined to listen to such revolutionary proposals and I felt irritated by his refusal to consider a new possibility.

Deep in my own thoughts, I did not notice Gwen Hardwick in her garden as I walked past.

'Good evening, Abey,' she called, looking up from digging out the root of a thistle that had sprung up under a plum tree.

'Evening,' I answered automatically.

'You sound lost in your own thoughts,' she called, straightening up and putting her hands on her back.

I moved my face into a smile and nodded, walking on. At that moment, with my present thoughts, I did not want to become involved in conversation with Albert's wife.

'How long will Albert be?' she persisted.

'He's talking to Abe Pullen. He won't be long,' I said.

'Are you all right?—I saw you at the school after the service last Sunday but you were talking to someone. There were a lot of folk there,' she persisted, so that I felt obliged to linger momentarily.

'Yes, there certainly were,' I answered, before adjusting my pace to pass out of her line of vision.

'Wait a minute, Abey!' she called.

I hesitated, considering whether I might get away with pretending not to hear, but Gwen's voice was not the sort that one did not hear. I looked back and saw that she was leaning over the little low wall.

'I promised to let Mrs Pickvance have some of my spinach. I've picked it ready and if you take it for me it will save me going round later.'

I waited by the wall while she fetched the bundle of spinach.

'You seem very quiet,' she said, looking hard at me. 'Are you all right?—What's on your mind?'

I shrugged. 'Oh, nothing, really. Just thinking,' I said.

'Albert says you went up to London the other day.'

I nodded.

She was still looking hard at me. 'I've told him to be careful not to lose you. He's worried about the work, you know.'

I nodded again but felt like saying 'Tell him to stop being such a stick-in-the-mud!'

'He thinks a lot of you,' she said. 'It must be

difficult settling back here, though.'

I went on nodding until she had finished, then said 'Times are changing. I shall have to keep up with them.'

I knew she would repeat this to Albert and felt I should leave it at that. I took the spinach and said I must go, as Mrs Pickvance would be waiting with my dinner.

That night we had a storm. I got up at two o'clock to look out of the window. The wind was howling and the trees on the green were swaying badly. I could hear dustbins clattering and I had to close my window to stop it rattling. When I took it off its stay I had to pull hard and hold it with both hands to stop the wind grabbing it. The rain came in a deluge suddenly, beating against the window. It came down the bedroom chimney and beat on the newspaper in the grate. I could hear water running fast in the gutters outside while great flashes of sheet lightning lit up the village as the slanting, driving rain lashed down on it. I went downstairs to see how Flossie was taking it and found her rolled up tightly in her basket. She was pleased to see me and quivered when I stroked her. She remained rolled up, whimpering when the thunder crashed. I carried her in her basket upstairs and set it down near my bed. I knew Mrs Pickvance would disapprove but dogs can be very frightened by thunderstorms and I decided to risk it. I lay in bed thinking, determined to do

172

something about my work situation. Perhaps I should have said more to Gwen Hardwick, in the knowledge that it would be relayed to Albert. Yet, in the ultimate I could not afford to lose my job and although I knew Albert valued my work he was not a man to change his decision if I threatened to leave. He knew as well as I did that the prospects of finding other work, even for a skilled man, were not good. The rain stopped suddenly and the wind dropped. I lay listening to the water still running in the gutters. After a while a patch of yellow moonlight fell across the wool rug on my bedroom floor and I could just glimpse a clearing sky through the window, which was at an angle from my bed. I thought I would get up and open the window again but Flossie at that moment, having got over her fear of the storm, jumped onto the bed and snuggled down somewhere near my feet. Visualising Mrs Pickvance's expression of horror, I fell asleep. Two hours later I awoke, terrified and sweating from a dreadful nightmare, where I was sinking in wet mud and slime back in the trenches with white-faced corpses sinking with me, while gunfire and explosions lit up the black and red sky. Trembling and wide-eyed, I clutched at the bedclothes until, slowly, I calmed down, to find myself in the early morning light staring at Flossie, who was sitting up watching me in alarm. I supposed thankfully that I had not cried out in my

173

dreaming, otherwise Mrs Pickvance might have come in to find the dog on the bed. All remained quiet. I patted Flossie to reassure her and lay back on my pillow, feeling exhausted and still unnerved by memories stirred by the nightmare.

At five o'clock I dressed and took Flossie downstairs. I lit the Primus stove and made a cup of tea. Outside, the garden looked ravaged by the storm and pieces of tree and flower petals littered the grass. I watched Flossie go round, sniffing the morning freshness and scaring the pigeons off the wheelbarrow. I sat dispirited at the kitchen table and drank the tea, staring at nothing.

I reached the workshop before Albert and walked to the back to lean over the rails of Magnolia's field. Magnolia and Jiffy were down by the stream. They turned their heads but remained where they were. I edged along the fence so that I could just see the memorial stone in the church wall across the road, too far on the angle to make out the names although I knew them by heart well enough. When I had passed there on my way that morning I had looked the other way towards the bakery as I was very conscious of the stone and its names. I wished now it had not been placed where I was bound to pass it every morning and evening. Now I stared hard back at it and, in the quiet early morning with the gentle breeze moving the tops of the elms, the lush, long, late-summer grass at my feet, I silently moved my lips to pronounce each name carved so permanently both in the stone and in my head.

'Morning, Abey,' said Albert as he walked past me, jingling the keys of the workshop in his hand. 'Quite a storm in the night.'

I followed him with Harry and Jes, who had joined us, and we set about opening up the shop. Bertie appeared on his bicycle and began dusting the previous day's dust from the windows before doing his stock feeding out at the back. Harry said old Ben's garden-shed roof had blown across to the allotments and that the rain had washed Horace's missus's gravel down onto her lawn.

As we hung up our lunch-bags a nephew of a farmer near Lonestock arrived on a bicycle to say a wheel on a harvest waggon had collapsed at their farm and needed immediate attention, and before he had finished giving his message a clanging and rattling cart from Froglies Green drew up outside. In the hot dry weather before the previous night's thunderstorm its old wheels had shrunk and finally distorted, leaving the iron tyres loose and the wheels in danger of collapsing.

'We're desperate for it!' said the man, beginning to take his horse from the shafts. 'How soon can you do it?'

'Can't look at it today!' said Albert '—And those wheels look like they need quite a bit of work on them.'

'I said you'd be busy about now but 'e said I were t'pressurise you!' said the man.

'Won't do no good. I've got two men up at Farmer Lane's this morning helping with the harvest and every man here has got his work being waited for. You tell John Henry that I'll see to it as soon as I can.'

Albert followed me into the shop and said 'You better go up to Lonestock, Abey, and see what needs doing there. Take Bertie with you. I'll see to the livestock. I said Albert Lane could borrow Magnolia today but you'll need to take 'er and the cart.'

I nodded and went to tell Bertie to fetch Magnolia and put her in the cart.

As we loaded up the jacks, blocks and levers that we might need, Saggy Palmer, who helped with the vicar's garden, appeared, looking agitated. 'Two of 'is pigs is got out in the night. 'E says somebody might 'ave stole 'em but I said 'ee'd 'ave 'eard 'em doing that, pigs squealin' like they do. They'll be about somewhere but I ain't 'ad no breakfast yet and they might not turn up fer some time!'

As he spoke a noise was heard beside the workshop where the sawbench and engine stood. There was another clatter.

Saggy ran round and shouted back 'Ah, 'tis them orright! Come and give me a 'and!'

Bertie ran to fetch a piece of corrugated iron from beside the blacksmith's and I picked

176

up a length of brushwood.

Saggy was calling to the two pigs. 'Come on out, you varmints!'

In a minute or so they peered cautiously out of their hiding place. We stood still, but at the sight of us they squealed and turned back. Only young they were, and excited by what they had done so far. A length of timber crashed down as they scurried back and some buckets rattled over.

Saggy's voice could be heard again: 'Get on out, you young varmints!—You be a-keepin' me from me breakfust!'

He poked at them with a length of scantling. Another squeal and they shot out, straight past us and towards the blacksmith's, where Peter Brookes had come out and was standing with another sheet of corrugated iron, to turn them back.

Just as they reached our shop again Albert came out. 'What's going on?' he shouted, scuffing his feet to turn the pigs away.

Saggy caught one of them with a broom handle he had picked up and with another squeal they turned, headed off by Bertie with his sheet of iron, and disappeared across the road in the direction of the vicarage. Saggy ran after them and we saw them no more.

'I thought you were getting off to Lonestock!' grumbled Albert.

'So we are,' I said.

'There's no time to be chasing pigs this

177

morning! Let the vicar come and fetch them himself! He's got nothing needs doing till Sunday!'

We finished loading the cart and set off. Being late autumn, the roadway was covered with leaves that the storm had brought down. Their reds and yellows were bright in the morning sunshine as they lay in a deep carpet under the turning cartwheels, while a few more trickled down from the hedgerow trees to rest upon our passing laps and load or to join the general strewing of the roadway.

'Where are we going?' asked Bertie as Magnolia turned towards Lonestock.

'Jamie Owen's.'

'I thought he still owed Albert for that new shaft.'

'Where did you hear that?' I asked.

Bertie shrugged. 'Everybody knows.'

'Lots of folk don't pay straight away,' I said.

'Last Christmas we did that job.'

I looked at him. 'If I'd said that to old Ben or Harry when I was an apprentice they would have told me it was none of my business.'

Bertie shrugged again.

'Some farmers don't have any money until harvest and it doesn't help them to pay if you don't repair their harvest carts,' I told him.

We passed Hawtin's old yard and cottage. It all looked very quiet and I could see from up on the cart that the front garden was overgrown.

Just beyond Lonestock the boy who had come to the shop was waiting with his bicycle near the roadside to direct us to the damaged waggon.

He led us through two gateways, over a stone bridge, round the side of a potato field and to the cart where it lay on its side with a broken shaft. We walked round it.

'Another broken shaft,' said Bertie, commenting on the obvious but wishing to impress the boy with the bicycle. 'We'll soon get that right.'

'Get the ropes out,' I said.

The cart had been loaded with sheaves of wheat and the horse, turning too quickly after it had crossed a culvert, had caused one wheel to slide towards the ditch. As the high load had swung over, the cart had twisted behind the horse, which was quite a young animal, making it stumble and panic for a moment. The result was that the cart had gone over on its side and broken the offside shaft, leaving it splintered and useless.

The first thing to do was to get the cart upright again. We did this by driving stakes into the ground just in front of the two wheels to prevent the cart sliding, then with a long rope over the top and attached to the far side, we fixed it to Magnolia's collar some twenty yards away. Bertie and I, using long levers, called to Magnolia, whose strength, weight and experience of such situations was invaluable.

179

Slowly the cart responded and was set upright again.

'See if your uncle can spare a horse to bring this down to Oldston,' I said to the boy, who nodded and went off on his bicycle.

We set about lashing a temporary shaft, which we had brought with us, to what remained of the old shaft. After a careful inspection I decided that no further damage had been done, so we put Magnolia into it and set about getting it to the roadway. Again, Magnolia's experience of temporary fixings was valuable and slowly she pulled it back to the gateway. Here we met the boy returning to say no horse was available as they were all at work in the harvest field.

'You'll have to come back for our cart then, Bertie,' I said as we set off through Lonestock back to the workshop.

At the shop Albert was waiting for us. Two more waggons had arrived since we left. I saw him knocking the dust from his hat as we approached. 'Put it over on the Rectory ground next to Tom Lovell's cart,' he called, pointing across the road. 'Help Harry to finish putting that new wheel on, then we can get one of these waggons in,' he said to me, then to Bertie 'Get off back with Magnolia and bring the cart down here, then take her up to Crossways for the harvest. Don't hang about! Get back as quick as you can!'

CHAPTER FOURTEEN

Harvest supper was always well attended and that year most folk from Nether Oldston were there. Held in the school, when the darker evenings were closing in fast, a friendly feeling of well-being was generated among the decorations and oil-lit lamps, while a mouth-watering aroma wafted from the school kitchen. Everyone knew everybody and everyone had given some thought to what they wore for the occasion. Baskets of rosy apples and a few prize bunches of grapes were placed along the centres of the trestle tables on their white starched table-cloths, and tumblers and tankards formed clusters at intervals. Big jugs of lemon barley-water stood brim full close by. A barrel of beer and a smaller one of cider were pouring forth, now that Bunker Cobham and Herbert Walker had finished driving in their wooden taps. Folded cloths, placed under the taps to protect the schoolroom floor, were already saturated and May Saunders was pushing through the thirsty group to replace them with dry ones.

We sang the usual harvest hymns with Albert Groom playing the accordion, then after welcoming everyone and saying grace, the vicar urged us all to give thanks in our hearts to God for his provision, to enjoy the sumptuous banquet prepared by our local ladies and to be in church on Sunday for the Harvest Thanksgiving Service.

After the meal we put away the tables and sat round to listen to Herbert Walker on his mouth organ and then Ticker Benson, estate foreman at Oldston Manor, who had a fine baritone voice, singing 'Little Grey Home in the West', accompanied by Albert Groom on the piano.

During the lull between these items Mr Luker drew a chair up to my side and asked if I was seriously going to do anything about furniture making, as he was interested in having a dresser made. He wanted something made locally and if I was interested I could call to discuss it with him.

'They've already started at The Central School this term,' he said.

I nodded. 'I can't see Albert letting me go now or in the future.'

'I go to London most weeks and my car takes me to Remsditch station two or three times a week and meets the train to come home. You can go and come in it, if you wish. You will need to pay the train fare.'

I looked at him.

He was serious. 'Look Abey, I'll come in tomorrow to ask Albert if I can get a dresser made in his workshop and I shall tell him that if I like it I shall be ordering some chairs. I shall also say I know of a workshop where I

182

can get them done but that I would rather have them made locally, providing they are done properly. We'll see what happens. If he says nothing to you about it you must make your own decision about what to do next but if he does, be ready to handle it. I enquired at The Central School last week and they said they would still consider a late starter, if he were suitable, before the end of this month.'

I had been sitting back in my chair full of good food and not a little alcohol, waiting to be entertained, and I was taken aback by this unexpected and forceful approach. Perce Chennel came along, carrying a refilled tankard of cider which he slopped just as he was handing it to me.

'Oh, right. Oh yes. Well, thank you Mr Luker,' I gabbled.

As he got up and carried his chair away, he said 'Think it over, Abey, and use the opportunity!'

The party over, the company dispersed quickly. Its mood, although the celebration had been appreciated, was a sombre one, for war memories were fresh and the deepening economic depression of the times was very real.

Next day I was not absolutely sure of what Mr Luker had said and wondered if he really would come to see Albert. But I saw him enter the shop just after the lunch break and head for Albert's office. Albert saw him, too, and

183

followed him. The door closed behind them.

'Harry's waiting for you to get them tyres off of John Henry's wheels with him,' said Bertie, coming up behind me.

'What! What tyres?—Oh yes, I'm coming.'

We had been unable to start work on the loose iron tyres that were waiting on John Henry's big waggon until today. Twice a message had come asking if it was ready to collect but pressure of work at the time had been too great. Dealing with a loose tyre was not uncommon and not complicated, providing it was dealt with before it caused harm to the wheel. In this case, however, all the wheels had been damaged by the rubbing iron and the spokes were showing through the fellies, which had also worn down and rounded over.

'One uv the wust I ever did see!' muttered Harry, 'Ought t'know better than that. 'Is dad would a given 'im a good 'idin before 'e died if 'e'd a knowed 'e'd a let 'em get like that!'

We set the waggon up on trestles and began to knock out the lynch pins that held the wheels on. Bertie marked each wheel with chalk: Right, Left, Near or Off, to ensure they would be put back in their same positions, then he rolled the first wheel away to the blacksmith's. Peter Brooks examined the wheel carefully to discover where the iron had been welded or 'shut' originally. It needed a practised eye to do this after so long wearing. 'There it is!' he said and marked it with chalk.

184

Abe Pullen came over and looked at it. 'Left 'em long enough didn't they?' he said to no one in particular.

He held the big wide cold chisel against the join. Peter raised his sledge hammer. Bang! went the iron rim as it sprang apart. The distorted tyre was levered off and the nails knocked out. Abe marked them with chalk so that the same iron would go back on the same wheel.

'Help 'em round with 'em, Jack,' called Peter to a young lad who was standing quietly watching. He had only started helping at the blacksmith's that week.

We carried the wheels back to the shop.

'Keep out of the way!' roared Abe as his grandson wandered across in front of us '—and leave them tongs alone!'

Mr Luker had gone when we returned and Albert remained in his office. We put one of the wheels up on the block and gouged back the ends of the spokes where they had come through or nearly so, then, setting up the wheel again, I held it with Bertie while Harry carefully trimmed the fellies level all round with an axe. This trimming was a highly skilled operation which I had not actually done before but now I had a go at it on the second wheel and managed reasonably well, although Harry finished it off.

Sally Pullen brought Owen into the shop to find me. 'He says he never thanked you for making that lovely wheelbarrow so I've brought him round to do so now,' she said. 'Come on now, here's Abey, now you thank him.'

'Bertie did quite a lot of the work,' I told her. 'He made the wheel and did it very well, too.' I nodded towards Bertie, who was holding one of the big waggon wheels for Harry, and she smiled at him.

'Dad says send the first wheel round as soon as its ready and not to wait till they're all done.' She looked round for Owen, who had gone over to Jes and was collecting long curly shavings from round his bench. 'Come on,' she called, 'leave them alone!—Look at him! Into everything, he is. Come on, we're going back to the smithy!'

Owen stood looking up at Jes and holding out a handful of shavings.

'You can have those, lad,' said Jes, laying his try-plane down for a minute and standing with his hands on his hips.

Owen looked serious for a moment then, giving a broad smile, went off with his treasures.

'We best put a new fellie in there, look, Abey,' said Harry, pointing to one part of the rim that was showing signs of cracking near the place where it was drilled for the spoke.

We made good progress with the wheels and worked on into the evening to catch up with the work. Albert came out to say he would lock up at seven but made no mention of Mr Luker's visit.

Then, towards the end of the following day when we were clearing up, he came over to ask me to see him for a minute before I left.

'Sit down, Abey,' he said, when I entered his office.

I put my dinner bag down beside the old Windsor chair and waited. His hat was on top of a heap of dusty papers. I wondered if some of those papers were the same ones that had been there when I had first sat in this chair as an entered apprentice.

'Now then, Abey. I've had an enquiry about making a dresser for Mr Luker up at Broughton Dagston. He says he knows the sort of thing he wants and it's to be in keeping with some stuff he's seen about. He's got friends in Gloucestershire and talked a lot about what he called 'Arts and Crafts'. I told him he should go there and get what he wants but he insisted that he wanted the local wheelwrights' skills and methods to be incorporated into the design of this dresser. Talked about the possibility of other furniture to follow, he did. I said we were too busy at the moment and it would probably be too expensive but I couldn't put him off. Said he was in no great hurry and hoped I would consider taking it on.' He stood up and walked across to the cupboard where the coach bolts and screws were kept. He closed the door and turned the big wooden button. 'He mentioned that you'd shown much interest in such furniture when you went up to see that place in London with him about the memorial stone.' He came back to his chair and sat down again. 'I'm not pleased about this, Abey. You know I've said we're wheelwrights and carpenters here and we can't take on other specialist types of work, especially fancy stuff like he wants. "A house divided, falls", and we already are not what we were here. Times are uncertain and I needs to gather my business strength together to continue, rather than diversify and become a "jack of all trades".' He stood up again and paced over to the window. 'If you want to change direction I can't stop you but I can stop you doing it here. You best look for somewhere else where they do more of what you're thinking of. I don't want to lose you, Abey; far from it; you've become a useful man and I value your work. If you go, I shall find it difficult to replace you but I'll have to try, of course. I thought you might settle down again in time and take a responsible role here. I know coming back here from the war has been difficult for you, and Gwen's told me often enough to be more tolerant, times being what they are.'

He turned round from the window and leant back against it. My empty dinner bag slid down the chair leg, flat onto the floor. It was quite dark now, although a pale moon was rising, and I began to feel cold, sitting there so long. We would be leaving soon and there was no point in lighting an oil lamp.

Outlined against the window, he continued 'We've got no experience with furniture here, Abey, no reputation for it. The market's not ours. People come with their carts and waggons because they know we can do it and because we always have done. How much furniture of the sort of price we'd have to ask would sell around here?' He walked back to his chair, picking up his hat in the darkening office and striking it against his knee. He cleared his throat after the dust had sunk to the floor. We sat in silence.

'The last thing I want to do is leave here, Mr Hardwick,' I said eventually. He made no comment on this and I went on: 'I understand what you've just said and agree with most of it, but while the local carpentry continues to be in demand, it seems a shame not to be ready to absorb some of the considerable skills of the wheelwright into more of a high-class individual product. I don't want to detract from the wheelwright's work, providing it keeps coming in, but you know as well as I do that the tractor and the motor-car are taking over fast, and while out here we might get enough work for years to come, it'll certainly change and we'll be left watching it do so—and where are we going to get replacements for men when they retire? Boys are not going to want to be apprentice wheelwrights for much longer.' Again he remained silent and I added 'There's no need to divide what we do. We could build on the good foundation that exists.'

'I've told you there'd be no market for it and folks waiting for their waggons wouldn't take kindly to seeing someone making a dresser while they waited to get their harvest in!' he said, and I knew this was true.

'But folks aren't waiting for waggons all the year round,' I persisted. 'We could see how it went at slacker times, and if we got going soon we could build up a reputation while we still had plenty of waggon work.'

'Farmers and folks like that wouldn't like it,' he insisted.

'You've always managed to combine the carpentry, the coffin making and the waggon work. This would not be very different, and it would strengthen your prospects, providing you did it to the same fine standards.'

'Folks would not take us seriously as furniture makers,' he said.

'Mr Luker is ready to,' I pointed out. 'It's people like him who are looking for stuff that's not machine-made that we could sell to.— Look, Mr Hardwick, when I went up to London I could see what was going on. The designs and superb constructions were everywhere at that art school. Why don't you let me go there for one day a week this winter

190

and get into it properly, to bring back here as a second string to the expert work we do here?'

Even in the gloom I was aware of Albert's eyes opening wide as he dashed his hat against his knee. 'What? Go up there one day a week! Who's going to pay you? And who's going to do your work while you've gone?'

'It would be an investment,' I said.

'It would be crazy,' he shouted.

I felt I had lost the argument. It was no good, I thought. We sat in silence while he pulled out the watch from his waistcoat, then 'It's time we went,' he said.

We got up and I tripped over my dinner bag, just saving myself from falling against the door. We walked through the deserted shop between the benches where Bertie had swept.

'Mrs Pickvance asked me to bring some eggs,' I said, suddenly remembering them.

'Ah, good thing you said. I've got to take some, too,' said Albert.

We collected the eggs and after locking up the main doors walked in silence as far as his house, when we bade each other goodnight and I continued to Number Three, The Green.

I had no way of knowing what was said at the Hardwick supper table that evening but I imagined that Albert either raved about my foolishness and impractical ideas or brought up the subject of Mr Luker's dresser with Gwen. Perhaps both. Whatever was said must have been quite different from what I

191

imagined, for very surprised I was by a comment of Abe Pullen's a few days later, when we were gathered around the tyring platform in the yard to assist with putting on John Henry's adjusted tyres.

The rims had been trimmed, a new fellie put in one and the joints between the fellies opened up a bit so that when the cooling iron shrank, it would pull up the spokes as the gaps closed. Peter Brooks was tending the circular fire round the iron and Abe and myself stood ready with Bertie, who had filled the cans from the water barrels, and Jim the new boy at the smithy, waiting with sledges, tyre-dogs and tongs.

'Don't stand there like that, you boys! Give a hand here!' shouted Peter at Bertie and Jim, and they moved over to help tend the fire, poking it to keep wood offcuts and old pieces of board burning round the heating iron.

Abe turned to me. 'Albert tells me you might be goin' up to London fer some training then,' he said casually. I was so taken aback by this that I was unable to reply and he, wondering if I had heard, continued 'I wonder he'll let you go. Not like Albert to do that. Shows we be in changing times!'

At that moment Peter called 'Ready!'

We moved closer and stood with the tongs waiting.

'Look out, lads!' he called, then with Abe's help the red glowing ring was lifted from the fire.

'Right!' called Peter, and they let the ring drop onto the ground to knock off any clinging clinker from the fire.

Immediately the three of us lifted it with tongs over the waiting wheel that was bolted onto the iron platform. A moment or two of suspense while placing it in position on one side of the wheel, as blue smoke shot up, choking and thick. I held it down while Abe and Peter struggled to push it down on the opposite side. Although expanded through the heat, it was still a tight fit and needed careful placing. As soon as it was in position over the wheel Abe took his sledge hammer and began knocking it down further onto the wheel. Peter and I held it down opposite to where he was striking. When it was further on Peter used his sledge to beat it quickly right into position. By now the wood was actually burning, with flames shooting up amidst the thick blue smoke pouring up all round.

'Water!' called Peter, and Bertie and Jim, who had been putting the next tyre into the fire, handed him the first canful. Abe grabbed another one and they poured the water over and around the burning wheel. Steam and smoke poured out and engulfed us all. The urgency of the process once it had begun, the smell of the burning ash fellies, and the constant threat that anything going wrong would ruin the whole wheel, stirred the adrenalin and provided an excitement special to this job. Any passer-by would stop to watch until the loud cracks from the closing joints and the rapidly cooling and shrinking iron had finished, leaving the rim blackened and the air pungent from damp, scorched ash. Quickly the wheel was unbolted and rolled, still very hot, to the water tank where it was lowered into the water and turned, until it had become completely and finally cooled.

When we started on the second wheel young Owen Pullen joined the watchers, and his grandfather more than once had to tell him to get out of the way, but it was an attractive scene for a youngster, with the ring of red fire, the smoke, the steam, the shouts, sweat and tension and the dangerously hot metal being dropped to the ground and then the clanging blows of the sledge hammers amidst the swirling smoke.

'When do you start school?' asked Harry, who had now joined us.

'Don't know,' said Owen.

'After Christmas,' said Abe.

'You'll like that then,' said Harry.

'No,' said Owen.

'What?—Why not?'

'Grandabe needs me to help him here,' said Owen, looking across at his grandfather, who was cleaning the face of his sledge hammer.

He nodded and said 'Ah, so I do, my lad, but you've got to learn other things, too.'

After the last wheel was done we left the boys to clear up and went back to the shop.

A dung cart with a broken tailboard was waiting for an urgently needed repair. As we wheeled it inside Greg Mottram followed us in.

'Albert's gone down the field,' Harry told him.

'Jes'll do then. Where is he?' asked Greg, going across to Jes, who was planing a piece of five-inch square beech for an axle bed. 'Tell him I want four good six-foot feeding troughs. They won't take you long, Jes. Oh, and by the way, the top rail on one of the goal posts up in the sports field is nearly off. See what you can do, will you, before it collapses?'

Bertie came back, bringing the last wheel with him, and we finished cleaning the four of them up so that George could paint them as soon as they were dry.

'Go and let Jes show you how to plane up that axle bed,' I said. Jes heard me and gave a little smile. It was not an easy thing to prepare. Dead square, straight and true it needed to be, and four foot six of hard beech was not easy to push a plane through especially as, being five inches thick, its top surface stood a little higher on the bench than usual.

All the while I wondered what might be deduced from Abe Pullen's earlier remark. 'Not like Albert' had been his summing up and, as I had considered the matter more or less closed, I was indeed surprised to think it still a possibility. I was soon to find out what were the implications suggested by Abe.

'The dogcart's out the front, Abey. I want you to come and look at some elm with me.' Albert stood inspecting the wheels we had put ready for painting. 'I see you had to put a new fellie in that one, then. Harry can get on with that tailboard. We shan't be long. Just over beyond Dagston up past the thicket near where that cow of Pearson Grantle got its horns caught.'

We got going, and when Jiffy was trotting briskly towards Broughton Dagston, Albert said 'What was all that about going on a day to London you were on about the other night?'

We reached the top of the rise and the little cart sped along. We passed Jim Bowler on his bicycle, who nodded while Albert raised his hand to him.

'Well,' I said, 'it seems to me that to be successful it would be necessary to learn the sort of direction that furniture design is taking. According to what I've been reading, a lot of new ideas and thoughts have developed since the war and although they were starting well before, it's only now that people are really taking an interest. There's a different line of thought now, what with wanting to leave the past behind and looking to something new. Furniture is beginning to reflect how people feel.' I was quoting something I had seen in a

196

copy of *The Studio* that Jimmy Townsend had sent me recently: 'A new interest in showing the beauty of material and construction is being linked with the need to forget the past devastation of our lands and people.'

The wheels crunched loudly from time to time as we swayed about in the fast moving dogcart and although I raised my voice I did not know how much Albert had heard. When I paused he nodded.

I went on: 'To get into the way of things I should need to attend one day a week, at least for a while, to study design, construction, finishing and modern tool methods.'

At this Albert shook his head slowly, after which neither of us spoke. After we had passed through the village he pulled Jiffy's reins a little to slow her and turned her through a gateway onto a cart track. The wheels fell silent as we continued towards the thicket and then he guided her round and across an open stretch of grass, over a fallen stonewall and up to a number of elms standing at intervals along a hedgerow. We pulled in near one of them.

We sat for a moment looking up into the branches of the tree, then he said 'I don't know, Abey. Things like this never came up in my father's day. We learned from each other and from those who had learned from those before them. Timber hasn't altered. The need to cut, season and shape it is still there. Design was never mentioned. The first time I ever heard it used was about that memorial stone, and I don't remember how to spell it even now. Then suddenly we don't seem as if we can go on without it. I should lose you for a day a week and I don't see how I can pay you for it. You'd have to get there and back and do with less money to do more with, and even then, if all that's overcome, I expect I shall lose you completely at the end of it.' Before I could answer he nodded towards the big elm and said 'That's one of them, look.'

He began to get out and I followed him. It was a big tree, the breeze moving among its thick branches and its first few yellow and red leaves fluttering down around us.

' 'Tis a good tree, this one,' he said. 'We should need a bigger bob than Israel's if we have it. The next two are not so big.' We walked over to look closely at them. 'What do you think?' he asked.

'They look all right. Very useful I should say,' I said. 'They might be difficult to get out to the road past that thicket and over the stones, but even if we have to cut the big one, it will be worth having.'

Albert nodded. 'I'll see if Israel can get hold of a bigger bob, then soon as they're down we'll get 'em away afore the ground gets too wet.'

We said no more about the London idea but I decided to put forward a scheme to him after I had sorted out the details.

CHAPTER FIFTEEN

First I wrote a letter to my father, explaining what I was hoping to do and asking him if he might be able to offer a little financial assistance. The answer came back, offering to make up the pay of one day lost each week for the next few months. I decided I would pay the school fees from my army gratuity. I wrote to the secretary and posted it that evening, then went to see Mr Luker.

'It's a good move, Abey,' he said. 'My timetable is flexible and I can almost certainly arrange to transport you one day a week to and from the station.'

I received a letter from the secretary pointing out that term had already started but that the principal would interview me on the following Monday at three-thirty. A timetable was enclosed showing classes together with a list of out-of-county fees. Furniture and workshop drawing were on Mondays with a Mr Spooner.

I waited until Albert was in his office and went in to see him. He frowned when I entered, as if expecting problems. I told him I had an interview next Monday afternoon, that I would need to attend each Monday each week of the term, that I could arrange transport and manage with one day's pay less.

His frown deepened as he listened. I added that it would not be my intention to leave him as a result of what I planned and I would give him my word that on the completion of my studies I would stay at least two more years with him.

'How long will you be going for?' he asked.

'I hope to the end of the session in July. They've started already.'

'Ah well, I don't know. This isn't the sort of problem I need. You better go to the interview, I suppose. Monday afternoon, you say. Come and tell me what they say.' He was still frowning when I left him.

Feeling quite excited, I told Harry and Bertie about it. Harry said nothing and Bertie wondered if he could come with me.

'Don't mention it at the moment!' I said. 'The whole position's very delicate.—If you've finished over there with Jes you can help me sort out some oak for a set of harrows.'

'London again!' said Mrs Pickvance. 'Whatever for?'

I told her.

'Ah, no wonder poor Albert's worried, then.'

'Is he worried, then?' I asked.

'So Gwen says.'

*   *   *

On Monday at midday I biked to Remsditch to catch the one o'clock train to Paddington.

As the train pulled in to the platform I heard a voice behind me call 'Abey!'

I looked round to see Charlotte Purton-Hentis being helped into a first-class compartment by her chauffeur. 'Good afternoon, Miss Charlotte,' I said.

'Hold on, I'll come along with you,' she said, and told her man to bring her case along to where I was heading.

We found a compartment empty, apart from two elderly ladies, and settled into it. 'Well, fancy seeing you here!' she exclaimed.

The train whistled and clouds of steam blew back, passed our window, as the engine began to crawl forward, making a great hissing sound.

'I gave up trying to visit you. You seemed too well guarded,' I said. 'I made enquiries but even that proved difficult. I thought you might have disappeared.'

'Sorry, Abey. It's not been easy with this damn leg. I've been living in London mostly since I came back. Daddy's turned his London house into flats and I'm in one of them. There's nothing to do in Oldston and everyone there fusses round me and stops anything happening. I can't drive the car at home but I've got a motor bike in London. I can manage it now, even with the dodgy leg. They took it off, you know, in the end. Lucky not to have lost the whole leg, they say.'

I looked at her. Apart from a few lines

201

round her eyes she looked remarkably well. The sparkle was back in her eyes and although the past had left its marks she conveyed that old enthusiasm again in her smile.

'But what are you doing and what are you going to the big city for?'

I explained.

'And you'll be going up every week then?'

'I hope so.'

'Wonderful! So you're settling back all right and obviously getting organised.' She looked at the opposite window where the steam was rushing past.

'Not really.'

She looked back at me. 'What? What exactly does that mean?'

'Oh, nothing really. Just unsettled. Everything's different.'

She shook her head. 'No, Abey. Everything isn't different. It's us. It's us that's different and we don't fit back in. I'm the same. I don't know what I do want. All the excitement, adventure, danger, fear, companionship has supplied too much adrenalin for too long. Dreadful though it all was, I miss it. I wouldn't want to go through it again but my system, my make up, craves for it.'

We sat rocking slightly sideways as the train crossed over points. For a few minutes we were silent. I knew she was right.

'What do you do in London?' I asked.

She gave a hollow laugh. 'I go to dances,

dinners, soirées, and manage quite well with my dummy foot. The rest of my time I help a cousin and her mother run a charity for ex-servicemen. Never a dull moment, and it stops me dwelling on realities most of the time.'

I nodded. I knew what she meant and she knew that I did. We both smiled and then sat quietly for some time looking out of the windows.

'I can't avoid facts with you,' she suddenly said.

I looked at her.

'That's why I've never contacted you. I'm frightened right deep down by the past and the future. You saw me at my lowest. I thought you might bring back the reality of all that.'

The train swayed through a cutting, then into a tunnel. The noise was deafening and I closed the windows of the compartment.

When we emerged again into the sunlight, I said 'I still have nightmares and find concentration difficult. I can't get back into what I was doing before. That's why I'm doing this, pinning my hopes on designing, and making good things to live with that reveal the beauty of "quiet shapes and simple forms".'

Charlotte looked hard at me. 'I haven't forgotten what you did for me that night in France, Abey,' she said quietly.

'They were momentous days, Miss Charlotte,' I said, somewhat confused. 'I just happened to be there.'

She shook her head and reached across to touch my hand. 'That was reality and you were there in it with me.'

I smiled. 'Life can never be the same. War's a sickening business and quickly gets out of control, but it does strip away false values and expose a lot of hypocrisy.' After a little silence, I added 'Fear and hunger leave their marks.'

The train was slowing down and shortly drew into Paddington.

'What time is your interview?' asked Charlotte.

'Three o'clock.'

'I'll get a taxi to Southampton Row. There's a good little café I know along there. We'll have some coffee. You'll just about have time.'

It was only my second experience of a taxi ride and I enjoyed speeding through the London streets. I looked at my grandfather's watch.

'They'll serve us quickly. You've got ten minutes,' said Charlotte.

She ordered the coffee as we entered and it came quickly. I was anxious not to be late.

'It's been good to see you, Abey. Go hard for what you want at your interview and good luck. I might see you on the train again.'

I thanked her for the taxi and coffee, adding 'Without the war I couldn't have shared either with you!'

She smiled at this as we parted outside on the pavement. 'Just along there is Theobalds

Road' she said, hailing the next taxi. 'And do call me Charlotte.'

I waved her off and hastened along to The Central School of Arts and Crafts.

*   *   *

At the reception office I was told to wait while the secretary was informed of my arrival. A little later I was taken to Mr Topping, who welcomed me and said the Principal would see me in a few minutes. I was nervous and somewhat aware that my mind had not been as concentrated as it should have been during my train journey and the coffee time with Charlotte. I had planned to think over what I might say and ask but now here I was, without any attempt having been made to prepare myself. A door opened.

'Good afternoon, Mr Staughton,' said Mr Burridge. 'Come through, will you.' We shook hands.

Seated in the Principal's office, I watched while he went behind the big oak desk.

'You're rather late to be applying for this session. Why is that?'

I explained that it had taken time to persuade my employer to let me come as his workshop was very busy and he was not sure he could afford to do so. Also, I said that he was concerned that I might leave him after having completed my indentures with him as a wheelwright and had now returned from the war somewhat unsettled.

He nodded. 'Furniture making you want to do, I understand, with a view to developing more along those lines?'

'That's right, Sir. I would like to see the wheelwright's skills and methods used in such work, now that a new awareness and enthusiasm for materials and honest construction seem to be growing.'

'Might you leave wheelwrighting, then?'

'It's not my intention, Sir. I love the trade and I would hope to encourage it as much as possible in the future, but I can see the effects of the motor-car and the development of the iron and steel industry. By offering the sort of furniture I hope to make, I see a strengthening of the local workshop and the remaining waggon and farm work to produce genuine, good standards and preserve the existence of experienced hand craftsmen.'

He asked what I had read lately, then went on to enquire about my travelling arrangements. He was of the opinion that it was rather late in the term to be starting and suggested that it might be more sensible to start in January, when he would be prepared to offer me a place for Monday each week.

I explained that I wanted to start while the idea was accepted by my employer. In January I would have to talk about it to convince him all over again, and also work was slacker in the winter months so it would be good to take advantage of that now.

He looked hard at me and nodded slowly, then said 'Come with me and see what Mr Spooner thinks.'

Mr Spooner remembered me and thought I might start straight away. 'You were the wheelwright, weren't you?' he said. 'All the practical work here is individual and you can catch up on the design and drawing. I can give you some notes to take away and browse through. They are duplicated on the jelly and rather faint in places but you could get most of what I've written.'

'Very well then, Mr Staughton,' interrupted the Principal, 'I'll tell the secretary to enter you for next Monday. I'll say goodbye now and leave you with Mr Spooner to sort out anything you might need in preparation. Call at the secretary's office before you go and arrange about fees.'

He shook hands and departed.

'I'll need to think about which tutor you will be with,' said Mr Spooner, 'but in the meantime have a look round at what everyone's doing and I'll find a few books for you to take away to look at. Perhaps you could decide about what to make before you come back, then we can sort out timber and get started on Monday morning.'

'You came back then!' said Robin, a young man who had shown me his work on my previous visit. He was now working on a bookcase with glass doors.

'What a beautiful piece of walnut,' I observed, 'but what are those white lines?'

'The stringing is holly. It's whiter than box and makes more of a contrast.'

'I like it. A nice size, too. Did you design it?'

He nodded. 'The drawings are in that folder. Have a look at them.'

I went to find Jimmy Townsend before leaving and he was delighted to hear I was starting on Monday.

Next morning I told Albert what I had arranged.

'Oh, ah. Oh well, we shall have to manage without you on Mondays, then,' he said and went over to help Jes move the elm sheep troughs so that the cart could pick them up to take to Greg Mottram.

Bertie was waiting to hear how I had got on, but a waggon had come in with a loose axle box and as it was holding up the carting of mangolds and the weather was likely to break at any moment it needed immediate attention. Harry and Albert Groom were completing repairs to cartwheels and farmers' men were waiting to take them away as soon as they were back on their axles. The rest of the shop was repairing broken harrows and a tailboard, all urgently required. The new harrows that we had started were held up for the moment but were ordered for use this month for winter seedbed preparation.

Fitzy Bluebottle came in and shouted 'Albert! You'll lose yer geraniums if you leaves them out any longer!'

Albert did not hear her and she turned to George Groom. 'Give me a hand with them, George. He's lucky not to have lost them last night with that frost!'

They carried the two wooden troughs of flowers round into the barn with Fitzy still muttering about such negligence.

' 'Ee's takin' on an extra 'and, then,' said Harry as he munched his bread and cheese at breakfast time.

'Who's that then?' I enquired.

'Well, 'ee's goin' t' be sort of a general 'elp, 'ee says. Come in yesterday, 'ee did. One of them as come to Bright's cottages after the war. Startin' termorrow.'

'Where's Jes?' I asked, noticing his absence.

'Up at Mottram's. There's new cow stalls goin' in up there. He's taken those sheep troughs up and gone to measure up fer the stalls.'

'Greg's doing well then, by the sound of it.'

Harry nodded. 'Ah. 'Tis them 'orses. 'Tis them as is makin' 'is money. Got 'is own stallion up there 'ee 'as now, yer know. Oh ah, Greg knows what 'ee's at, all right. There's more than a bit of 'is old dad in Greg. 'Orses is in 'is blood.'

'Tractors will take over from them, though,'

said Bertie.

Harry looked round at him. 'Not yet they won't, boy. Not before my generation be gone, they wun't and what's more, older farmers want more 'orses now than ever t' replace them as bin lost in France.'

'Can you spare a couple of evenings, Abey?' Simon Gathercole was sharpening his chisel as I walked past his bench. 'We want to get the end barn ready for putting the poultry in and me dad's not up to moving the stuff that's in there. I'm going to put some glass in the windows, too.'

I was hoping to spend some time with the books I'd brought home from London but found myself saying 'Yes, all right, Simon. Ask Bertie as well; he'll probably come.'

Simon examined the edge of his two-inch chisel for a moment then, after putting a drop more neatsfoot oil on the surface of the stone, continued rubbing. 'Do you know Bart Cross?' he asked.

'Who?'

'He's starting here tomorrow. Lives up at Bright's Cottages. Lost an eye and part of his face at Passchendaele.'

'I've seen him about.'

'Been out of work since he came back.'

He turned the chisel over to lay it on the stone and 'flat it off'. Examining it again, he wiped the oil off and stropped it backwards and forwards on the palm of his hand.

'Albert reckons he'll be useful all round now we're getting busy again. Nellie Hawtin was here looking for you yesterday. Said she'd call in again.'

Albert came over and told me he had bought the elm we looked at and that it was coming at the end of November. Israel was bringing a bigger timber bob which he reckoned would handle the big tree. 'Soon as we've finished these pressing jobs we'll get squared up in the yard ready,' he said.

Greg Mottram came in and asked Albert how soon he could make him a dogcart.

Albert looked at him questioningly. 'I heard you was buying a motor,' he said.

Greg shook his head and winked. 'So I am. A fine one too. Coming it is next week but my missus says she won't have anything to do with it and if I wants her to go on she'll have to have a little dogcart to go to market and about in.'

Albert took his hat off, scratched his head and knocked his hat on his knee. 'Well, 'twill take a week or two. Soon as this bit of a rush is over, Abey could make a start at it.'

The deal was made and I thought that Albert, and indeed the whole workshop, seemed more cheerful than of late, in spite of the darker nights and coming of winter.

As I was about to leave that evening Albert came to see if I might give him a hand with the milking as Freda Parsons, who normally did it,

211

had been kicked by a new heifer and had gone home. I quite enjoyed the task as a change, although my hands were not now used to such activities.

That evening, there was a trace of frost in the air when I rode my bicycle back from the Gathercole smallholding. The moon was bright enough to see quite clearly so I had not lit its carbide lamp. I had to pass the cottage of Nellie Hawtin. She was sister-in-law to Mr Hawtin up at Lonestock, a widow who had lost her only son on the Somme. As I pedalled past she called out 'Is that you Mr Staughton?'

I pulled up just past her cottage and she came up to me.

'I seed you a goin' earlier and I bin watchin' to catch you. Miss Harbottle said as I should ask you. Can you spare a minute?'

I was still hoping to get an hour or so on those books but I leaned the bicycle against the wall and went in.

'I hope as you won't mind me askin' you but my sister, she's been taken bad. Up in Leeds she is. I got to go see 'er. She's real bad. I can't get there and back in one day and I got no one to milk my goat, Biddy. I did wonder if you'd be so kind as to do it for me. 'Twould be evenin', termorrer and the next mornin' like?' She stood nervously wringing her hands together. 'I wouldn't have asked you but I didn't know who else 'ud do it and Betsy did say she was sure you wouldn't mind, like.'

212

'Yes, all right. Show me where everything is,' I said.

She showed me, telling me that Biddy would stand 'good as gold' on the wooden box that her husband, Jack, had made specially for the purpose, out there in the shed. 'Mind you, 'er bag's got so low now that I uses this 'ere basin. It goes underneath nicely. She won't put 'er foot in it nor nothing. She's very good.' She showed me the flat enamel pie dish I was to use, then taking me along the garden path with a hurricane lamp we peered into the shed. 'There she is, look. You say 'ello to 'er. She likes a bit a green stuff. I'll put cabbage and apple there ready with 'er 'ay and mixture measured out ready.' As we left Biddy bleated, and stood on her hind legs to look over the low door of the shed. 'She won't hurt left inside till I gets back. Give a drop of the milk to my 'ens up there at the top of the garden and throw them a 'andful of corn. Take the milk to Mrs Pickvance. I shan't need it.'

She led the way back into the cottage. 'You will have a cup of tea now won't you, Mr Staughton? I've got it all just ready. Look, the kettle's a-boilin'!'

I thanked her.

'Sit yourself down a minute. I expect you've bin busy all day. I hear that Mr Cross is startin' with Albert. He's a good man. He would a' helped with Biddy but he can't milk, you see.'

She stirred the teapot and set it to draw.

'Mrs Pickvance tells me you be goin' up t' London regular like. Some sort of trainin' is it, then?'

I nodded.

'Ah well, I expect you needs to be keepin' up with new ideas, although Albert doesn't seem to need anything different.'

She poured the red-brown liquid from the teapot and handed me the brimming cup. I tried to sip it but its fierce heat drove me back with a stinging tongue.

'I expect old Wilbur Gathercole's gettin' ready fer bringing in 'is poultry. You bin up there 'elpin', I daresay. He seems to have more poultry than ever this year. Mind you, 'is son Simon does a lot of it now. 'Ee usually asks me to help with the pluckin' be now. Ah well, perhaps I be gettin' too slow.'

I persisted with the hot tea and eventually finished it.

I rose and thanked her. 'I'll come tomorrow evening then,' I said.

'Are you sure you won't 'ave another cup?'

I declined.

'I'll leave the back door unlocked but you won't need to come in. You can get round to the back through the side gate and I'll put everthing ready in the shed.'

She thanked me again as I pedalled away. The moon had disappeared but I didn't bother to light my lamp.

CHAPTER SIXTEEN

Mr Luker came to see if we were going to make his dresser and Albert told him he had better have a word with me. I told him I had meant to come up and tell him what had been happening but so far it had been impossible.

'There's no hurry,' he said.

'I hope to talk about it to Mr Spooner at the first opportunity and that Albert will agree to it being made here in the workshop after the design has been settled.'

'That's fine,' he said. 'I would like it to be made in oak but I will leave you to discuss that as well.'

'I can't get to you tonight but perhaps Thursday or Friday evening I could come up and see where it is to go.'

'Certainly, and I shall expect you to be waiting for my motor-car to pick you up on Monday morning for the station.'

After Mr Luker had left Albert asked what I had told him.

'I said I would prepare a design and if he liked it you would produce it here.'

'A bit high-handed that was, Abey,' he said, knocking the dust out from his hat against his knee.

'You told him to see me about it, which meant you would take it on, as you knew I was

215

prepared to do it,' I said.

He replaced his hat and, after looking out of the back doorway where the hens were scratching amongst the odd pieces of straw dropped by Bertie, said 'Ah well, we shall see.'

Then, looking round at me, he told me 'Bart Cross started this morning. He's out there now with Bertie seeing to the stock and things. I want Bertie to join you more now. Bart will do the feeding and so on but I don't want you leading him away from the wheelwrighting. He's got a lot to learn and we need another good man trained in our methods. I don't want any dressers or anything else made until after Greg Mottram's cart's done, nor while there's pressing work on waggons and the usual stuff.'

I nodded. 'We need some more belt dressing for the engine when Mr Shrives calls next,' I told him.

'I'll put it on his list,' he said.

At tea break I told Simon I would be a little late coming up as I was going to milk Nellie Hawtin's goat on the way.

*   *   *

Biddy bleated and watched over her door when she heard me getting the stuff out of the shed next door to her but when I went in to her she moved over to the far corner. Brown and white, elderly and with quite impressive horns, she wore a collar, which helped, as I

216

needed to lead her up onto the milking box. At first I thought she was going to refuse to get onto it but after a moment's hesitation she stepped up and put her nose into the feed bucket. I did not know if Nellie usually tied her up so I took the precaution of doing so. Her bag was certainly close to the ground. When she walked forward she had to step up and over it at each side and looked somewhat comical in motion. Nevertheless, she produced a good yield of milk: nearly three pints, which I had to keep emptying from the pie dish into a milking pail. When she had finished her meal she turned her head right round and eyed me carefully, making me feel somewhat self-conscious. It was mostly finger and thumb work and very tiring for hands not used to it. As I toiled I felt the need to talk to her. When I emptied the pie dish again I stopped to rub her nose but she withdrew it and shook her head before eyeing me again, as if to say 'Stop that nonsense and get on with it! I've never known anyone take so long!' At last I finished and when I released her she jumped down and went to wait near the hay rack. Mrs Pickvance had said she did not want the evening milk so I took it with me for the Gathercoles to feed to their poultry.

Thinking about my own work, I decided I would make a small writing bureau which would be useful in my room at Number Three for future studying and storage of papers.

*   *   *

On Monday morning when I awoke I was excited by the prospect of what I felt hopefully might prove to be a new, worthwhile phase in my life. It was still early and I had plenty of time before Mr Luker's car picked me up at 6.15. As I sat drinking my cup of tea with my sandwich box and notebook in my bag, watching the streaks of light appearing beyond the darkened sky, my mood changed and I sat in thought for a moment in the silence of the morning. Damp and dripping with mist, the sycamore in the garden was already shedding some of its keys, making patches of yellow and black on the grass. I thought of my father and brothers who would be tying up their cows ready for milking and I thought of the mud of the trenches. I remembered cuddling Marie under the heavy tarpaulin in the railway truck and I heard the soldiers singing as they passed us in their open train. 'He shot her and himself,' said a voice. What I was now embarking on seemed pointless.

Then Flossie moved closer to my legs as she heard Mrs Pickvance on the stairs.

As she came in, wearing a bedcap over her pipe-cleaner curlers, with a dark brown dressing-gown wrapped around her, 'Are you all ready, Abey?' she asked.

Flossie moved back to her basket, wagging

218

her tail, and was told to stay there.

I heard the car draw up outside, patted Flossie's head, thanked Mrs Pickvance and said I hoped to be back about 7.0.

At nine o'clock there was much hustle and bustle in and around the entrance to The School of Arts and Crafts. Students carrying portfolios and bags crowded the steps in the doorway and as I went in I felt quite excited by the prospect that I was now, at least in some way, part of this sensitive and vibrant vanguard of design and craftsmanship.

'Abey!' called a voice and Jimmy Townsend appeared. He slapped me on the back. 'You made it then. Good for you! I'll be in the canteen at break. See you then!' and before I had said a word he was gone.

Mr Spooner showed me where I would be working and introduced me to my tutor. I was told to go to the drawing office to look at books and photographs of furniture, then make sketches of my ideas for a writing bureau. Mr Spooner came in from time to time and discussed possibilities and construction. During these discussions I mentioned the proposed dresser for Mr Luker. He suggested I should make sketches for this in the coming week and he would look at them next time before making working drawings.

The day went very quickly and in no time I found it was Tuesday morning and I was back in Oldston sorting out ash for the Mottram dogcart.

Bertie was aware that my absence on a Monday needed playing down in the workshop and talk about London and furniture making was best done discreetly. However, he was unable to restrain himself from plying me with questions when we first arrived in the morning. I told him I would tell him about it later. Bertie was proving an apprentice with a very definite natural aptitude for the work we were doing. It enabled him to quickly grasp the underlying principles of cart construction and develop the necessary skills involved in making. He was frustrated by my answer and scowled while we turned over the ash boards.

The dogcarts we had made in the past had all been the same as the first one I had helped old Ben make before I went to the war. Now, I suggested refining this one slightly by making it with panelled sides.

Albert nodded enthusiastically and, after saying that he had ordered the springs and shaft fulcrums from Joseph Richards in Birmingham and that Abe Pullen had already made most of the other metal fittings, he said 'There'll be enough nice walnut to make panelled sides round behind the apron cupboard. I'll help you get it out.'

While I set out the sizes on the walnut Bertie carried in the ash that I had selected for the bottom boards. I gave him the dimensions and told him to plane them up.

At tea break Fitzy came in to say Nellie Hawtin wanted to see me and told Albert to remind Gwen to bring a table-cloth to the Women's Institute meeting that evening.

Bertie was struggling to plane the ash. He was trying to take thickish shavings off but they were tending to jam in the mouth of the plane because he had not set it properly. I told him to set the back-iron a little wider. The back-iron in a wooden plane is set by using a screwdriver to loosen the big iron screw that holds the specially shaped iron to the back of the cutter or cutting iron. The position of one to the other is set according to the work in hand, and generally, the finer the work, the closer the back-iron is set to the cutting edge. After sharpening, the plane has to be re-set and this is something that comes naturally after some practice. It is done after the position of the back-iron has been set, either by tapping with a hammer at the back of the plane, which moves the cutter up, or on the top of the cutter to set it down. The plane is held upside down to look along the sole to assess the setting of the cutter while one's thumb is kept firmly against the cutter and wooden wedge to prevent them falling out. Finally a smart tap from the hammer drives the wooden wedge in firmly again.

Albert asked me if I had learned anything in London and I told him I was working on drawings for Mr Luker's dresser and that it

221

was most likely going to be in oak.

He nodded, then told me 'I've just been round to see Freda Parsons. She's not coming back to milking yet. Fred says she's not to come back at all but she says he'll get over that in a little while. Makes it difficult, though, with Bart not able to milk. I can't afford the time to keep doing it myself.'

'Why don't you ask Nellie?' I said. 'She can milk and might like to do something.'

'What, Nellie Hawtin?—I shouldn't think so,' he said.

'You could try. I'll ask her if you like. I've got to call there,' I told him.

'Well, you can mention it then, if you like, but I shall be surprised if she will. Anyway, I wondered if you would do it tonight, Abey.'

CHAPTER SEVENTEEN

Christmas came. I went home for two days but before going away I called to see Nellie Hawtin and she insisted on making tea while she told me how much better her sister was, what a fine city Leeds was with its big noisy station and how well Biddy looked after my care of her.

'Mind you, she did bleat and bleat like I never did hear before to welcome me back, Mr Staughton,' she said.

'You be goin 'ome fer Christmas then. Ah well, your folks'll be glad ter see yer.' She looked down at her hands in her lap and went quiet before adding 'Christmases aren't the same now fer me.' Then she stole a quick look at the photograph of her son on the mantlepiece. ''Tis four Christmases without my Eddie now. 'Ee milked Biddy for me that last Christmas when he was on leave. "You 'ave a day off, Mother," he said. "When I comes 'ome fer good we'll get a cow and one or two other things with my savings from the army," but he never come back from the Somme. I had a letter from his officer to tell me what a good soldier he was.'

I nodded and we sipped the tea in silence for a moment. The square oak-cased clock on the mantlepiece next to the photograph gave a clunk as its mechanism prepared to strike the half hour.

'My 'usband, when he was dying, said "Young Eddie will soon be old enough to look after you, Nellie; he's growin' up quick",' she said, then added quietly 'Too quick.'

'Albert wondered if you might be able to give a hand with milking at the shop,' I said.

'What, me?' she asked, frowning.

'Just while Freda Parsons is away.'

'Oh I don't know, Mr Staughton: 'tis the other end of the village and I got my own things to see to.'

'I said I would ask you. You could think

223

about it, anyway,' I said.

She looked thoughtful as I got up to go. 'Afternoons might be possible, but mornings, I dunno.'

'You think it over, Mrs Hawtin. You might enjoy it,' I said as I left.

When I returned from Christmas I found her milking both mornings and afternoons.

'Not fer long, Mr Staughton. Just till Freda gets back,' she told me as she emptied a bucket of warm, frothy milk into the churn.

*   *   *

Soon after starting the new term in January at The Central School I decided it was better to cycle to Remsditch to catch the early train because it enabled me to stay for extra evening classes and return when it suited me. Drawings were produced for the writing bureau and for Mr Luker's dresser. I learned to use the T-square and set squares on the drawing-board and how to produce elevations and plans, how to line in with drawing pens using Indian ink and finally colouring with water-colour washes. Later, I was shown how to coat paper with a bromide mixture and make blueprints from tracings of my drawings by putting them in a glazed frame and standing them out in bright sunlight.

Mr Luker was very impressed when I showed him his proposed dresser. Albert, too, when I laid the drawings on his desk stood nodding in silence before going on to say that all the metalwork for the Mottram dogcart was ready and waiting.

I did not see Charlotte again on the train before Easter but towards the end of February I received a short note by post from her London address. 'Dear Abey, I am running a charity show here in four weeks' time. Can you help with chairs and things?'

I replied 'Probably, but it will depend on times and date.'

The following Monday when I went to eat my sandwiches in the canteen I found Charlotte sitting there, talking to two young ladies while she waited for me.

She came across when she saw me with Robin and Jimmy Townsend. 'Hello, Abey! I got your note and came to see if you could make it three weeks from Saturday, about ten o'clock. Here's the address but I'll get someone to collect you from Paddington if you come up that morning.'

I was taken aback so merely said 'Oh yes, all right'.

Robin and Jimmy had gone very quiet and as I struggled to collect my thoughts Charlotte said 'Are you going to introduce me, Abey?'

'Oh, yes, er, this is Robin Styles and this is Jimmy Townsend. Both friends and students here.'

'Hello,' she said, 'I'm Charlotte Purton-

Hentis. Friend of Abey's. Live in the same village. He's going to give me a hand for a do I'm having. I must away, though.' She rose and pushed her chair under the table. 'Stay for the evening, Abey, if you can. There's a dance in the evening. Bring a girl friend if you like. See you Saturday week, then.'

Robin and Jimmy looked at each other as soon as she had gone and raised their eyebrows. 'Ah ha! He's a dark horse, that Abey Staughton!' said Jimmy.

'You're right there. He seems to have got things nicely set up here in the big city. "Bring a girl friend as well," eh?'

I wondered how on earth I could arrange to be there on that Saturday. Albert would almost certainly be awkward about me having a morning off, as he was still very conscious of me being away on Mondays.

The bureau was taking shape. The oak I was using was a very attractive brown timber showing beautiful medullary rays in some of the boards, which should look very good with the linseed oil finish I planned for it. In the past I had seen Horace cutting dovetails but I had never had occasion to use them myself until now. The tendency in furniture design of the art schools at that time, when the Arts and Crafts Movement was so strongly influenced by William Morris, Philip Webb, Ernest Gimson and William Lethaby, our own past principal of The Central School, was to show its construction, so the use of through-dovetails and through-mortices and tenons was encouraged. Natural wood colours for furniture was popular, too, to reveal the beauty of the grain. To consider staining anything branded one a philistine.

My hand and eye were well experienced for the task of accurate sawing and chiselling and after a little instruction as to the proportions and setting out of the dovetails I was able to make my first attempts for the corners of the carcase, and was pleased with them.

*   *   *

I discovered that with the principal's permission a daytime student could stay on for an evening session without incurring extra cost. To allow for this, I made a habit of taking a couple of extra sandwiches and ate them with a mug of tea in the canteen between sessions.

The following Monday when I was sitting there one of the girls that Charlotte had been talking to came in. She collected a mug of cocoa and sat by the window. I thought she was probably waiting for her friend. After a little while I went across to refill my cup and as I passed I thought she gave a little smile.

I stopped and asked her if she knew Charlotte.

'Yes, I do,' she said. 'She has a flat near

227

where I live with my parents and I meet her on Red Cross work doing library duties at the local hospital.'

'Ah, I see.—May I sit here?'

'Of course. I nearly spoke to you when I came in, but I didn't like to.'

'What are you doing here?' I asked.

'Embroidery.'

'Oh.—Where's your friend this evening?'

'She has influenza.'

'I'm sorry to hear that.'

'Thank you. I'll tell her.' She went on 'What are you doing?'

'Furniture making.'

'That sounds interesting.—Charlotte said you're going to help her with a dance or something.'

'Yes. That's true, but I don't know yet how I'm going to get time off to do it.'

We talked about what we did and she told me she was attending classes in the evenings. Her name was Laura and she worked in the accounts department of a big London store. She spoke with a north-country accent, having lived in Northumberland before coming to London for munitions work at Woolwich Arsenal during the war. Her friend was a trainee manageress in a Lyons Corner House restaurant.

On the train going home and again on my bicycle to Nether Oldston I found myself thinking more about Laura than about the design lectures and dovetails that I had been involved with all day, and the wish occurred to me that I was in a position to ask her to go to Charlotte's dance with me.

*   *   *

Bertie had helped Albert and Jes to prepare the yard for the new timber while I was away. Albert would not let him work on the dogcart without me, although he could quite well have continued with the assembly of the bodywork, which was nearing completion. The panelled sides in walnut looked very well and I saw Albert standing looking at them once or twice. Bertie wanted to know what I had done in London and when I was going to start making the dresser. I set him to fix the tailboard while I worked on the wheels. Old Ben had always made the wheels that were finer than the ones for carts and waggons, but since the first light wheels I had helped him with, I had become quite proficient at them; my experience had grown steadily and now I was enjoying the fashioning of these more graceful items. When they were finished, with their lighter iron tyres, and varnished with a fine black line painted round each by Albert Groom, they were very attractive, particularly when the sunshine fell upon the turning spokes behind a high-stepping pony. I learned that American wheels of this lighter nature were often made without the slight dish shape we built into them but we agreed that our method produced a much stronger wheel, more able to stand up to the battering from the hard road surfaces here. In America they tended to be used more on soft earth surfaces.

Israel Parker called in to tell Albert he was coming to move the timber a week on Friday. 'That is, if the weather holds,' he said.

'Why not bring it this week?' shouted Albert, as if he could make Israel hear him.

'Friday week then, about ten o'clock,' smiled Israel. There was no arguing with him. He could lip read to some extent but the local dialect with little or no lip movement and so many heavy moustaches made that almost impossible. I wondered how the original requirements were got through to him. Certainly it was easier to go along with his propositions once they were formed. If anybody could make contact with him it was Jes, who used various expressions, signs and pointings.

As Israel stopped at Jes's bench on the way out Albert shouted to him 'Ask him why not do it this week while the ground's hard.'

'He says the big bob is over near Launprindle until the weekend and then he's taking it to Dagston. He might come Thursday if it goes well. He'll let you know on Wednesday if he's coming earlier than Friday,' called Jes.

Israel nodded and smiled to confirm this. 'See you next week then, Albert!' he called, and waved goodbye.

'Humph!' exclaimed Albert, which everyone heard except Israel.

We finished the dogcart by the end of the week and Bertie very much hoped that Albert would let him work with me on the dresser next.

'You get started on the varnishing, Abey, and Bertie can go up to Trows Farm to help Jes get on with the new cow-stalls up there,' Albert decided.

Bertie scowled as soon as he had gone. 'He knows I want to do the furniture work!' he complained.

'There's some good work to be done up there,' I said. 'You can learn a lot from Jes like I did, and anyway he hasn't said anything about me starting the dresser yet, and Jes reckons he's nearly finished at the farm.— Take Magnolia with those bits of elm and get a move on, young Bertie. Jes will be waiting for them.'

As he went out to call Magnolia Bertie gave a final scowl, while I began the long varnishing process.

The finish on the dogcarts made in the workshop was of a high standard. It required a dust free atmosphere and some careful brushwork to work out the clear varnish evenly, without any runs at awkward corners or edges, to finally show off the grain of the ash and, this time, the walnut sides. Five coats of goldsize followed by three of varnish, flatted well in between coats with pumice, would take a number of days as the varnish was slow to dry in the winter. We would paint the wheels and metal parts dark blue, then give the whole thing a coat of clear varnish. When it was dry, we would swill it over with cold water to harden the varnish. Since the war we had bought the blue paint ready mixed but any other colours for the carts and waggons we still mixed ourselves from ground powder colour, oil and turps. The back of the paint shop door was covered with thick brushfuls of old paint where colours had been tried out.

As I left the village early the following Monday morning it was light enough for the district nurse on her bicycle and me to see each other and she waved to me. I noticed she turned in at Abe Pullen's house and wondered what had prompted her to call so early.

During the previous week my thoughts about asking Laura to Charlotte's dance had grown into a strong desire to do so. That day my work progressed well and I also went to an exhibition with Robin to see some pieces of furniture that Mr Spooner had designed, but my main concern was with Laura. I eagerly looked for her in the canteen during the evening but I did not see her or her friend and by the end of the day I realised I had missed her. I rode back to the village through heavy rain and wind later that night feeling very disappointed.

After peeling off my wet garments in the bicycle shed I was surprised to find Mrs Pickvance waiting for me in the kitchen.

'Young Owen Pullen's got diphtheria,' she said.

I stood looking at her.

She nodded. 'Doctor's been and nurse is still there now. Bad he is too, they say, poor little chap.'

'What ever will they do?' I asked and she shook her head. I knew that Sally and her parents would be beside themselves. Their household revolved around the little boy.

'You be late again, Abey, 'tis nearly midnight, look. You'll 'ave a job to be up by five-thirty. I've boiled the kettle and while you get them wet socks off I'll make you a cup of Bovril. Then I'm goin' to bed.'

I patted Flossie and took the hot cup up to my bedroom with me.

Tuesday morning was too damp and foggy to continue varnishing the dogcart so I set about sorting out some oak for the dresser. I had noted some one-and-a-quarter inch boards stacked away at the end of the straw barn. They had been cut from the centre of the tree and those just to the side of the centre gave a good twenty inch width. There were seven or eight boards about ten feet in length.

The middle ones cut virtually on the radius showed the medullary rays which are associated with first quality oak and which we all referred to as 'flowered oak'. The very centre board contained the 'pith' or remains of the original sapling which, being soft and unreliable, would need to be cut out to provide two narrower boards. The figure or 'flower' is only revealed by cutting along the radius of the tree. Boards sawn in this way are known as quarter-sawn, and offer greater stability, less distortion when drying out or seasoning and are best for important work such as cart shafts. More waste is involved and so it is a more expensive way of converting timber from the tree. Quarter-sawn oak was often referred to as wainscot oak, the word wainscot deriving, I was told, from the German word for waggon shaft. It was often selected for decorative purposes for wainscots besides featuring prominently in church work.

This particular oak was good and dry and I suspect might have been put away by Horace with a view to some other purpose. As I lifted the last dusty board from amongst the straw and stood it against the wall with the other ones, Albert came in.

'Ah, there you are, Abey. I see you've found them boards, then. I was going to suggest we might use them for Sendersby house. There's some work to do on the panelling up there.'

'It's too thick for panelling,' I protested.

'We might need some a bit thicker for part of the framework and there's a door needing attention as well,' he said, brushing aside some dust with his hand from one of the boards and peering closely at it. 'What had you got in mind for it, then?' he asked, as if he did not know.

'Luker's dresser.'

He looked at each board then removed his hat and striking it against his knee set up enough dust to start us both sneezing. ''Tis good stuff. 'T'would be a shame to waste it.' He went on: 'How much would you need?'

Irritated by all of this, I said shortly 'All of it.'

'Well, that's that, then. We'll have to find something else for Sendersby,' and with that he replaced his hat and went out of the barn.

I decided to go ahead unless he stopped me, and set about carrying the heavy boards into the shop.

'Nice stuff!' observed Simon. I nodded, and took out the cutting list I had prepared previously to start marking out the pieces.

A little later the weather brightened up and I continued varnishing in the paint shop.

Peter Brooks came over for kindling wood and told me that Abe was very distraught. 'Won't speak, nor nothing. The vicar's bin in this morning to see him. I heard him telling him that kids can get over it and that prayer will enlist the powerful help of the Almighty.'

'What did he say to that?' I asked.

'He just stared at the anvil for a minute. He never spoke. He went over and started raking the fire. We've got six horses out there a-waiting fer shoes this mornin'. That'll keep his mind off things for a bit, but I don't think he went to bed last night.'

CHAPTER EIGHTEEN

The night before Israel Parker was due to come over with the timber bob we had a light fall of snow. The Friday morning was bitterly cold with a wind that cut like a knife. Everyone including Albert, I think, thought and hoped he would not come but surely enough a message arrived with a lad on a bicycle to say he was on his way. Albert told Bart to give the boy a cup of cocoa then all of us except Simon, who was left to look after the shop, and Jes and Bertie who were fortunate enough to be up at Trows Farm finishing off the mangers, were marshalled together by Albert. We wrapped ourselves up with everything we could find and set off with Magnolia and bicycles.

The ground was good and hard. Israel was waiting for us and had lit a little brushwood fire to keep himself warm. His six big black shire horses had their nosebags on and he had stood them with their backs to the wind, sheltered slightly by a cluster of hawthorn. We were all soon involved with moving the trunk of the biggest tree. The question was whether the bob was big enough to handle the diameter of this particular log. The wheels were just over eight feet in diameter and six inches wide. It would depend on how far into the ground they sank when the weight of the log was lifted. Chains and levers, pushed and pulled by men and horses, helped to angle it. Two of the six horses and Magnolia were used to move it to where the huge wheels could straddle it ready for lifting.

The golden sun rose higher into the cold blue sky and between the sparkling white trees and brushwood a cloud of mist evaporated above each striving man and beast. The men pushed and pulled the wheels into position over the log. One very long, heavy pole rose from the axle of the wheels and was set pointing upright, which angled the shaped riser between the wheels to lay back on the log. Chains were attached from under and round the log to the riser so that when the long pole was pulled down the log would be lifted. The men stood either side of the pole, Magnolia was attached by a long rope to the end of it and as I eased her forward the men all pulled down on the pole. The frosted ground under the wheels compressed. It cracked and the wheels sank heavily down. For a moment the pole and the log did not move, then the earth sank no more and the front end of the log was raised a few inches and the pole was brought down.

'Hold 'er down!' called Israel to the men clustered round the end of the pole as he and Albert began chaining it down to the log. A smaller set of wheels was lashed to the other end of the log. The first wheels had been positioned just ahead of the centre so carried most of the weight. The six horses were harnessed in pairs to the front of the timber bob, straining as they thrust their shoulders into their collars. As the great wide wheels rolled, pressing into the crinkling earth behind the flying feathered feet, the sky darkened while the wind still blew. I remembered the gun-carriages. The desolation around the fallen trees, where scattered brambles had been dragged and cut up over the disturbed earth, stabbed at my memory. I saw the men as soldiers and shivered violently with fear for a moment.

'Snow comin',' said Harry, seeing Ben looking at the dark clouds sweeping over the sky.

'Ah, shouldn't wonder,' said Ben.

'Come on, keep up with it, push where you can!' shouted Albert, and we all ran alongside and behind the moving timber until it reached the harder, more compact track that led to the roadway.

At the road there was some discussion as to whether the log would be better transferred to a timber waggon, but it was decided to continue with the bob, slow and cumbersome though it was. Whether Israel understood what was being said I could not tell, but when Albert gave him a nod he positioned Albert, Harry and myself to walk with the load and carry skidpans ready to hold the load back on downhill stretches.

I heard him telling Albert that the horses' shoes had all been roughened by the smith at Launprindle to stop them slipping on the frosty roads. 'Too cold fer snow,' he said, slapping his hands on his sides as he went to lead the front horses.

Slowly, slowly we proceeded. Through Dagston, even more slowly down the hill into Oldston. The other men were making up a load of the bigger branch trimmings for firewood and would bring Magnolia back when they were ready. As we turned out of Tiptoe Lane to pass by The Green into the High Street and as Israel walked backwards, leading the horses so he could watch the load take the corner past Mrs Pickvance's house, murmuring 'Steady now, steady!' there was an almighty bang! One side of the load dropped and stopped dead while the other side, trying to continue, skidded round slightly. The horses, sensing something wrong, had stopped pulling even before Israel shouted 'Woa!'. The nearside wheel had broken. Two spokes had collapsed, letting the iron tyre bend enough to break the fellie at that point.

Israel uttered an oath as we regarded the damage.

'Get the load off quick!' said Albert.

Rapidly the horses were unhitched, the pole allowed to rise and the log lowered.

' 'Twill have to come off,' said Harry and Albert nodded. He made signs to Israel indicating taking the wheel off and Israel nodded gloomily. Magnolia and the others had caught up with us now and gathered round the broken wheel. Mrs Pickvance came out to look and so did the landlord of The Barley Mow as well as a number of children.

'Better get on with it then,' said Mrs Pickvance. 'We don't want it there all night!' It was blocking the road, but by leading Magnolia round the green after Israel had moved his horse team, the cart could just get past. We quickly unloaded the firewood and took the jacks, levers and blocks to set the axle up on while we took the wheel off.

' 'T'would 'ave bin worse along the 'igh street,' said George. 'Nothin' would 'ave got past, an it'll be there fer a day or so.'

Back at the shop we got the tyre off and sent it round to Peter for truing up. Harry and I set about repairing the wheel. Two new spokes and two new fellies were required and the removing of the old tenons from the stock took some time. Great big fellies and spokes they were. It was a slow business finding suitable pieces as we seldom had a call for anything so big. Cleft oak for the spokes was not too difficult but suitable ash for the fellies took a long time, and even then Harry shook his head doubtfully when we settled on a piece. It was dark well before we had even cut out the pieces. Bertie, who had returned from Trows Farm with Jes, was sent to put red hurricane lamps at each end of the load while we worked on the broken wheel into the evening. Peter agreed to come back after his evening meal to put the tyre on if we had finished. Meanwhile, Israel had stabled his horses at Crosswood Farm.

We finished late under the oil lamps. Peter came back and waited until we finished. Bertie also stayed on to help.

Round at the forge Peter told us as he pumped the bellows that he had not seen Abe that day. 'Sittin' up there with that little lad, he is. I saw his missus this mornin' for a few minutes. "Won't eat nothin'" she said; "just sits and stares at the boy". The nurse tries to get him away but he won't move. Nurse said the next day would prove vital. She's bin there day and night fer the last two days. They've put a tube in his little throat and she has to watch it doesn't block up.'

Harry, Bertie and I all helped Peter to try the big heavy tyre against the repaired wheel.

241

'Needs half inch takin' out,' said Peter. The old weld was found, that part of the iron was put into the fire and coals were heaped up over it. Bertie was sent to gather enough stuff to get a big enough fire going to heat up the eight-foot circle.

'My brother died of it,' said Harry.

Peter nodded. 'Abe won't get over it if anything happens to the boy.'

We took the iron from the fire and laid the white, glowing part on the anvil to hold it there while Peter cut through it. It sprang slightly apart and while the glowing, heavy iron lit up his perspiring face in the semi darkness he quickly chopped off the unwanted half inch. The iron was put back in the fire to prepare it for welding. Albert came in with cups of cocoa for us and helped prepare the big circle of fire to heat the whole tyre. This was a long job and we sweated hard over it, but eventually it was fitted, driven on with sledge hammers, when like mediaeval witch dancers around the smoking, burning circle we poured water over it to quench the hot iron and blackened wood. Tired, we put the nails in and left the wheel ready to trim next morning.

We fitted the wheel back onto the timber bob before daylight next morning so when Israel Parker appeared with his horses it was ready to continue its journey. Israel decided to use only four horses now as the road was good and level along the village and it would enable the whole cavalcade to get round into the lane and across the field to the workshop yard more easily. In the early morning light the massive load ground heavily along the lane with Israel walking backwards, stopping and starting the champing horses to avoid the log hitting the corner of the baker's.

'Good thing the bark was taken off first!' joked Harry, as we pulled into the yard amidst shouts and snorting horses.

Across in the blacksmith's yard we could see the doctor's car outside the Pullens' house.

'Woa! Woa!' called Israel, and the horses came to rest, champing on their bits, dipping their heads and shaking their manes. Their backs steamed in the cold air and they blew clouds from their wide, velvet nostrils as they rattled their brasses and harness. The wooden structure bearing the load creaked and settled. I had watched every revolution that the new section in the wheel made and now it stood looking pretty good as eager hands untied ropes and unbuckled chains. The load was lowered and the wheels removed. Peter came round with young Jim to help lever the log away to where it would await the sawyers.

'Any news?' I asked.

'No,' said Peter. 'Doctor's bin there all night. Don't look too good.'

'Too big! Logs like that be too big fer handling here!' complained Harry. 'The sawyers won't like it!'

'We'll get off for the other logs, then,' said Israel.

'Come up a bit later, Abey,' said Albert. 'Mrs Maycock's coming in this morning to see about us making a shield to put up in the village hall with the names of WI presidents on it. I thought you would handle that. Don't give her a price, though, until I've seen what it is.' He climbed up with the other men behind Magnolia to follow Israel.

Only Simon was with me in the workshop. He was replacing a splintered floor board in a muck cart. I did not want to be halfway through a coat of varnish on the dogcart when Mrs Maycock appeared so began planing some of the oak for the dresser.

'Sounds like the doctor's motor going,' called Simon.

We stopped and listened. I nodded and went to look outside. Then I went round to the smithy to ask Peter what had happened.

He shrugged his shoulders. 'Never saw him. He shot off in his motor without a word. I went out but he looked straight ahead and drove away.'

Simon had followed me. We stood wondering, then to our great surprise Abe Pullen came in.

'He's goin' to be all right!' he shouted. 'Doctor's just gone. Bin with us most of the night he has, but he says he's past the danger point. He's going to be all right.' His pale face, with eyes sunken and cheeks hollow from lack of food and sleep, was now radiant with smiles. He stumbled, and Simon guided him to a bench where he sat down heavily. His big shoulders shook as he began to cry. He wept and wept. No one tried to speak. Peter went across and put a hand on his shoulder. Simon and I went back to our shop, thanking God for his mercy on Abe Pullen.

*   *   *

On Monday evening I sat with Jimmy Townsend in the canteen between sessions at The Central School. He had found a back number of *The Studio* recording the death of Ernest Gimson, whose work as a furniture designer I had come to admire. 'The Arts and Crafts Society has lost one of its most valued members' it began, and finished by praising his furniture because it 'never failed to elicit admiration by its logical simplicity and conscientious workmanship, and it is safe to predict that in years to come these productions will be as eagerly sought after as those of the great cabinet makers of bygone generations.'

I had just finished reading it when Laura and her friend came in. My pleasure at seeing Laura was tempered by the wish that her friend was not with her. The two girls brought their cups of cocoa to sit with us and Laura introduced her friend, Amy.

'Are you still hoping to manage next Saturday?' asked Laura.

'Yes, still hoping,' I said, wishing I had mentioned it to Albert.

'I'm thinking of joining our local ramblers' association,' she said, smiling.

Jimmy frowned. 'There's been trouble with ramblers back where I live,' he said.

'Oh, what sort of trouble?' asked Laura.

'I think it's just that there are so many of them. They swarm over the fields and along the tracks. Gates get left open and hedges trampled. Nothing malicious but farmers don't like it.'

I nodded. 'I know my father doesn't like too many folk on the footpaths.'

Laura pulled a face. 'I haven't been yet so you can't blame me! Anyway, it's all supposed to be very orderly and while enjoying the great outside, you're supposed to respect the farmer.'

Jimmy shrugged. 'I went home last week and the village was overrun with them on Sunday afternoon. Sitting about and peering everywhere. Mother said not one of them went to Evensong in the village.'

We finished our refreshments, and still I hadn't said anything about the dance. But as we made for our various rooms I had a sudden glimpse of my train journey and bicycle ride home that night. Knowing that I would have thrown away the last chance through my faint heart, as we parted in the corridor I took Laura's arm and blurted out 'Would you come to that dance with me?'

She looked slightly startled.

'What, on Saturday night?' she exclaimed.

I nodded, unable to find any more words.

'Well, I expect I could,' she said hesitatingly.

I tried to say 'It starts at seven' but only 'Seven' came out.

'Yes, but how shall I meet you?' she asked.

I had not thought that far. 'Well, er . . . address here,' I managed to come out with, then added '. . . somewhere.' I began shuffling in my pocket.

'You would have to fetch me,' she said, looking doubtful.

'Would I?' I said, then, faced with the possibility of her changing her mind, added rashly 'Of course! Give me your address and I'll pick you up at seven.'

'I expect it will be evening dress?' she asked.

'Oh, yes, probably.'

'I can easily find out,' she said. 'It's not very far from where I live. I'll send you a postcard to let you know.' She smiled and touched my arm. 'I'll look forward to it!—I must go! See you Saturday. Make it a quarter past seven; I don't want to be the first there.'

She ran after Amy and I stood as if in a trance. People pushed past me in both directions. I walked towards the workshop, wondering at first what I had done and then

247

feeling more and more excited as I realised just what had happened.

Now I felt elated. I did not know what sort of dress would be required, how I could get an evening suit if that was what was needed, how I was going to get time off to go, how I could afford to take a young lady with me and how I would get home afterwards. But I did not care! I had surmounted the most difficult factor; that of asking Laura, and Laura had accepted! I would cope with anything else!

I found it difficult to read or put my mind to my studies in the train later that evening, pedalled like a supercharged racer when I left the station for Nether Oldston, and hardly slept any of the short night before arriving at the shop the next day.

CHAPTER NINETEEN

'Them Mondies in Londun don't do yer no good!' pronounced Harry, when my eyes momentarily closed during the morning tea break.

'Left the lid off the varnish he did!' joined in Bertie gleefully, but Harry rounded on him.

'You be quiet, boy! You got too much to say fer y'self. I wasn't allowed t' say nothin' when I was a 'prentice.'

I had just completed the last coat on the

dogcart. Five coats of goldsize each rubbed down with pumice, and then three coats of clear varnish. Albert Groom would paint the ironwork and wheels dark blue and it would be finished.

I was cleaning out the brushes when Albert Hardwick came in. 'Begins to look well, Abey,' he said.

I nodded and decided to plunge straight in.

'Miss Charlotte's asked me to help with a charity concert in London but it means going up on Saturday,' I said, wiping out a brush on a piece of rag.

Albert looked at me.

'What, this Saturday?'

'Yes.'

'What time?'

'I'd have to leave in the morning.'

'You won't be here at all soon!'

'I can make up the time in the evenings and following Saturday.'

'I've got a motor coming in tomorrow for some repairs and alterations to the bodywork. I was going to put you on to that next.'

'Yes, all right. Where's that from, then?'

'The carrier up at Sendersby, Stevie Barton: changing his horse for a motor and wants one of the doors made to take off and a new bearer putting in where the tailboard lets down. But what about the dresser?'

I felt that this was a step forward, in that the dresser was now, 'the dresser' instead of 'your

249

dresser', implying that the shop was accepting its production. 'I was going to get on with it now,' I said.

He nodded. 'I saw where you've been planing that oak, lovely stuff!—But you'll have to leave it when you start the motor waggon tomorrow. Bertie can help you later. He's helping Simon to get the wheel off that water cart.—What did Mrs Maycock want last week?'

I had forgotten about her. 'Oh,' I said, 'she didn't come.'

'She will!' he said, and went out into the yard.

When I had finished in the paint shop I went to see if Bertie was available, but found he and Simon were having a struggle removing the linch-pin from the axle that held the wheel on, which could be difficult if the pin had been there for a long time. I told him to come over to me when Simon had finished with him.

Half an hour later George brought Mrs Maycock over to my bench.

'Good morning, Ma'am,' I said brushing aside some of the shavings and straightening my apron.

'Good morning, Mr Staughton,' she replied. 'Mr Hardwick has told me to discuss the Women's Institute Shield with you as you'll most probably make it. Nothing too fancy you know, Mr Staughton, but large enough for plenty of names and dates and smart enough to command attention and imply importance.'

I nodded, and indicated the blackboard at the end of the shop where the shape of a field gate had been drawn to show dimensions. I felt for a piece of chalk in the big pocket of my apron as she followed me past Harry and then past Jes, to whom she said respectively 'Good morning, Mr Teemer,' and 'Good morning, Mr Beales,' while they each in turn mouthed 'Mornin', Ma'am.'

I found a space on the board and suggested a shield shape.

'More curve on the side, perhaps,' she suggested, 'and some sort of scroll on the top, I think.'

I changed the shape a little and waited.

She looked critically at it for a moment then took the chalk. 'Where's the duster?' she asked, looking round. She spotted the piece of whitish rag and shook it out, causing a cloud of white dust to envelop us both. 'Good gracious!' she exclaimed and withdrew a few steps until it had settled. 'More like that, look!' she said, carefully handling the rag and altering the top corners.

I nodded.

She stood back with her head on one side, looking at it. 'Yes, I think that would do. That would be about the right size, too.' She chalked in the position of several names and dates. 'Last for twenty years of presidents,' she said. 'Now, I want it painted dark green with gold lettering and scrolls.—The next important meeting is just four weeks today. That should give you plenty of time to get it up on the wall by then, with Mrs Tringham, our first president's name, on it.'

She smiled slightly, presumably visualising the chalked drawing transformed into the green and gold shield on the schoolroom wall.

'What will you charge?' she suddenly asked.

'I'll have to discuss that with Mr Hardwick. He'll let you know in a day or two.'

'Where is he?'

'Out in the field; and it will take a little while to work out the price,' I said.

'Tell him to keep the price down; it's for a local good cause and his wife's on the committee,' she said, gingerly setting down the dusty rag and backing away from it before blowing and clapping her hands disapprovingly. At the doorway she stopped for a moment to dust herself down again before stepping out into the village street.

Bertie joined me to help with the preparation of the oak and the rest of the day was spent with some heavy planing, sawing and regular sharpening of plane irons. At the end of the day while Bertie swept up the shavings I showed Albert the WI shield drawing.

He nodded when I told him what Mrs Maycock had said. 'You'll have to do it after Stevie Barton's motor waggon. Shouldn't take you long.'

In the next day or two I received a postcard from Charlotte, saying 'I will telephone you at the post office at 6.15 on Thursday, C.P.H.' I was there and waiting at exactly that time, when the bell rang. 'Abey, I bumped into Laura Penfold on Monday. She says you're bringing her to the dance on Saturday. Splendid! She asked about dress. It's evening dress. Have you got a black tie and dinner jacket?'

'No,' I said.

'There are two or three spare ones here. One is sure to be about your size. Shirt as well. Bring studs and cuff-links.—What train will you be on?'

'Arriving nine o'clock.'

'Good. You can stay here afterwards. My man, Jenson, will meet you at Paddington. Wears glasses, grey hair, Aston Martin two seater, light blue upholstery. There's going to be a lot to do on Saturday morning. See you then. Good-bye.'

Outside the post office I met Jenny Hawtin. 'Abey, I haven't seen you lately. Don't forget the concert on Saturday. We'll need some help with chairs in the afternoon and I also wondered if you would be able to collect the Primrose League cups and saucers from up at Dagston. I daresay Albert Hardwick will lend you the cart.'

'Oh Jenny, I won't be here on Saturday—' I began.

'What on earth do you mean?' she said.

'I shall be in London.'

'What, on Saturday? What for?'

'I've agreed to help Charlotte Purton-Hentis with a charity concert and dance up there.' I did not feel able to tell her that I had forgotten the village concert.

Jenny's mouth opened wide and for a second she was struck dumb.

I felt an absolute heel.

'I don't believe it!' she began. 'Folks here have been rehearsing and working to provide some entertainment for the village and you arrange to be somewhere else, helping Miss Charlotte Purton-Hentis of all people, who's never raised a finger for folks here! Well, on behalf of everyone, thank you very much for nothing, Abey Staughton!'

'But Jenny . . .' I began, but with that she turned about and stalked off furiously, with her head in the air.

I had not mentioned my extra London trip to Mrs Pickvance before doing so to Albert Hardwick. No doubt if I had, she would have reminded me about the village concert being on the same evening. Not that I would have been able to change anything, but I might have said something to Jenny before this and avoided such severe displeasure.

Now I did tell Mrs Pickvance, knowing that she would have read Charlotte's post-card when it arrived earlier in the week. She was no more sympathetic. 'I knew no good would come of spending time up in London. No man can serve two masters!—What ever time will you be back, then?' she said, banging her broom on the back doorstep and making Flossie slink back to her basket, looking anxious.

'I'll stay the night with some friends.'

'Oh, I see! Well, let me warn you to take care! That Miss Charlotte's not been seen nor heard of round here since the war. Charity work, you say; well that may be! Anyway you be careful!—Have you told your mother you're going dancing in London?'

'Mrs Pickvance, I appreciate your concern for me but I'm nearly twenty-seven and I've spent nearly three years in the army. I will be careful!'

Still frowning, she shook the brush and banged the back door hard, while Flossie wriggled lower into the blankets of her basket.

*   *   *

By the end of the week Bertie and I had cut out and planed up all of the oak for the main dresser construction, and had finished the work on Stevie Barton's motor waggon. This had been a matter of removing the offside door and fitting lift-off hinges so that the door could be left at home for his rounds as carrier but put back in position when taking his family out at the weekend. Also, one of the castings holding the long tailboard pin at one end had become loose, where water had caused rot in the wooden bearer. We replaced this bearer with a sound piece of straight-grained ash. Then we sorted out some lime for Bertie to plane up on Saturday morning, ready for me to start the WI shield on Tuesday. Lime is a good material for carving; rather characterless, holding up well on edges and corners, yet constantly mild working.

On Friday evening Mrs Pickvance ensured that I had packed enough clean clothes for the next day. I wondered about shoes and socks. My best black shoes were rather heavy for dancing, I thought.

'What about black socks?' asked Mrs Pickvance.

'I expect I shall be able to borrow some,' I said as I had none.

'Take them dark blue ones,' she said.

'Oh no, they must be black.'

'They are nearly black; they'll do,' she said, but I shook my head and closed the small attaché case.

Whether it was excitement or not, I do not know, but I woke after midnight trembling with fear and pouring with sweat. Mrs Pickvance was by my bed with a lighted candle.

'You'll be all right. Have a sip of water,' she was saying.

I had been dreaming of khaki-clad bodies among barbed wire and slime. A huge black tank-shape with great clanking caterpillar tracks had loomed over me as I looked round feverishly, fearing to be enveloped and squashed into the dark, evil-smelling mud. I tried to crawl through the bedclothes, feeling them as heavy as mud, bogging me down before the advancing destruction.

My shouting had brought Mrs Pickvance out of her room. 'Abey, you're here in bed at Number Three. Look, it's your room!' she was saying: 'Sip the water. You're all right. It's safe here!'

Gradually I calmed down, and began to feel cold. I drank the water but could not stop shivering. She sorted out the bedclothes which I had mangled into a heap and I lay down again while she tucked me back into bed.

'You'll be all right now. You'll soon get warm again. Try to get some sleep.'

She went back to bed and I lay in the dark, the dreadful reality of the nightmare still clutching at me as I stared into the darkness.

*   *   *

'I don't know when I shall get back,' I said as I patted Flossie farewell next morning.

Mrs Pickvance had got up to see me off.

Clutching her tightly wound dressing-gown and wearing her snood over the rag curlers, she stood in her old, worn slippers with her bare legs like sticks holding her up. 'You make sure you get some proper breakfast!' she was saying, 'and remember what I said about London and everything!'

I tried a little smile, which was not easy at that time in the morning, but received only a continuing frown.

She stood back when I opened the door, holding Flossie's collar. She nodded as I closed the door, making me feel quite guilty. The resentment that welled up in me was because I knew my concern for her was deep and she made me feel like a naughty disobedient child.

I fixed my case to the carrier and lit the lamps on my bicycle; occasionally the village policeman would rise early and stand watching for offenders in the early morning darkness. The wind was blowing cold and was against me to Remsditch but the train was warm and comfortable.

I was met by Jenson in the Aston Martin and whisked off to a church hall in south east London.

'Who are you?' asked a young man when I entered.

I opened my mouth to answer but he wasn't listening. 'If you're helping, see if you can get some of those chairs down from the gallery. Put them here, behind these other ones.'

Another man joined me. 'What time does the concert start?' he asked me.

'I don't know,' I answered.

'No one seems to know anything,' he complained.

'Who's in charge?' I asked.

He shrugged. 'Everyone's round behind the stage, making that noise. Last minute rehearsal, they told me. "Go and help move the chairs," they said. I wish I'd stayed in bed.'

We moved chairs all morning, tying them together in rows with long battens behind them. Someone brought us coffee and shortbread at one point and I thought of Mrs Pickvance and 'proper breakfast'.

'Hello, Abey darling!' called Charlotte's voice from somewhere. 'Lunch is at the Black Horse opposite.'

The hall was cold, and a desperate effort was being made to fuel two big iron tortoise stoves in readiness for the concert that afternoon.

'Keep the doors shut!' was constantly shouted.

At about 1.30 six helpers and some of the cast, with Charlotte among them, met at the Black Horse to eat sandwiches and drink beer.

'Are you in the show?' asked a man called Gerald, who had appeared about 11.30 and had tied chairs with me until lunchtime. He had shown interest in the fact that I was a wheelwright. 'A labourer in the vineyard, eh?'

he had said. 'Before I came home from France I said I was not going back to an architect's office. I wanted to get to grips with materials other than paper! But the flesh being weak, I returned to the old drawing boards.'

I told him I was not in the show.

'Come with me, if you like. I'm playing rugger for Croydon at 2.30. We're playing Blackheath. Should be a good game. Come and watch.'

I managed to get near Charlotte to speak to her at one point.

'Where can I pick up the suit for tonight?' I asked her.

'After the show come back with me or, if you like, ask Jenson when he comes back to take you home to find it for you. He knows about it.'

I decided not to watch the rugger and instead saw the show, which included some very good acts and attracted a full house.

The dance that evening was at a neighbouring hotel but the hall had to be cleared after the audience had gone. The same team, plus a few and minus Gerald, set about returning chairs to where they had come from, clearing the stage and sweeping the hall. While helping, I watched out for Jenson.

'If you're ready, Sir, I could take you now,' said Jenson, as the last broom was put away.

A large house in Brockley, set back impressively in its own tree-lined, gravelled carriageway, had been divided into two flats. Charlotte's part was expensively furnished and decorated. A housekeeper showed me the bathroom and told me a meal was waiting.

Jenson led me to a bedroom. Indicating a wardrobe, he said 'Your requirements should all be there, Sir. If there is any difficulty, pull the bell.'

The wardrobe contained at least four suits and many other items. Collars, shirts, bow ties all lay on shelves. But there were no shoes or socks.

I went to wash, then joined two other helpers who had arrived to be fed before getting ready for the dance.

It was six o'clock when I went to sort out the suit that fitted me best. The trousers were all too long and the most suitable required the braces being set uncomfortably short. I struggled with the bow tie over the winged collar but failed miserably. Then there was the question of socks. Mrs Pickvance had stuffed the dark blue pair into my case after I had closed it and they had fallen out as I opened it. I regarded them against the black trousers. They were quite dark and I thought they might not show much under the long trousers so I decided to put them on, rather than ring the bell and make a fuss. I had never worn sock suspenders but thought I would try the ones in the wardrobe. I found them uncomfortable and one came undone to trail over my shoe when I tried walking about. I took them off, relying on the long trousers to cover the socks, which were wrinkled as well as blue.

'Where's your bow tie, Mr Staughton?' asked Mrs Rawlinson, the housekeeper, when I came out into the hall.

I put my hand up to my collar, having forgotten to make another attempt at tying it.

'Go and fetch it and I will tie it for you,' she said, smiling.

Charlotte came in, looking tired. She refused a meal but ordered a brandy with soda. 'I'm going to sit with my leg up for half an hour. Everything went splendidly and everyone did so well.' She went on 'Ah, Abey, I've hardly seen you. Thank you so much for coming.—You found everything, then. How are you getting over for Laura?'

'I'm told there's a bus which takes me to the bottom of Harefield Road,' I told her.

'Oh no!' She called Jenson and told him to take me to Harefield Road to collect Miss Penfold when I was ready to go. Then, to me, she said 'Come and sit with me while I drink this, Abey.—I won't be up before midday tomorrow. Just get up and Mrs Rawlinson will give you breakfast before you go.' I thanked her, and said I would do that.

'I saw you with Gerald in the hall. He's a good sort. Lost three brothers in France. Training to be an architect.'

'He said he would be there tonight,' I said.

'He got an MC at Passchendaele,' she said, looking at her wristwatch. '—What time are you meeting Laura?'

'I should be going now,' I said standing up and straightening my jacket.

'I think there's a white scarf in that wardrobe,' Charlotte said.

I fetched it and put it on as I had no coat and it was quite cold.

CHAPTER TWENTY

For the next few hours I lived out a dream in which I played the part of a young gentleman. I remember that as I stepped into the Aston Martin in my uncomfortable cutting trousers, blue wrinkled socks and too clumpy shoes, I thought of the old Cinderella story.

Laura was waiting for me, dressed for the dance and looking breathtakingly beautiful, ready to play her part for the whole fantastic evening. Nothing seemed real. We stepped into the foyer of the hotel to descend the decorated stairway into the ballroom. The band was playing and before I had caught up with my thoughts I found myself attempting to foxtrot.

'It's easy!' Laura said. 'Just follow the music and count: one two, one two three!'

I struggled, conscious of my tightly braced

trousers and my clumpy shoes, and tried to count.

The mood was overwhelming. I forgot the trousers and the socks; I was entranced by the smiling, laughing girl in my arms and began to pick up the rhythm of the relentless ragtime music and foxtrotted, quickstepped, charlestoned and waltzed, swaying and swirling ever more expertly as the evening progressed.

During one of the breaks between dances when we sat among some of the friends from the afternoon, Gerald, who was now accompanied by a dazzling girl friend, introduced as Mabel, went with me to collect drinks from the bar. 'Charlotte tells me you're at The Central School doing furniture design.'

'Only part time,' I said.

'We're doing a new wing on a country house near Oxford. Furniture as well. Just finished the drawings for the building. I thought you were in wheelwrighting.'

'So I am,' I said and as we returned with the drinks to our table I explained a little of my involvements.

Charlotte did not attempt dancing but sat with a friend from the city, who seemed to know everything about the new developments in a scheme for regularly flying passengers to and from the continent. He consumed a steady supply of whisky.

The hours raced by and the evening disappeared. When the last waltz was announced I was amazed to see it was a quarter to two. Dancing with Laura in my arms, I was aware that the magic was about to end. The lights were dimmed, the swish of the dancers swept softly to the strains of 'Let me call you sweetheart', and I became aware of a strange sensation. I felt that it was Marie I was holding and dancing with. I looked down in the soft, warm light and thought I could see Marie. I held Laura at arm's length rather suddenly. She smiled reassuringly and we danced on. The band brought the waltz to its conclusion and Laura looked up at me, bright-eyed and gorgeous. We stood still for the national anthem and clapped again. She squeezed my hand as I led her from the dance floor.

Soup was served before leaving and then we said our farewells to everyone. We sat in the back of the Aston Martin enjoying the darkness, my arm around Laura, emboldened by the cold night to huddle closely together. The all-too-short journey to Harefield Road ended and we climbed the steps to her front door.

'Thank you so much for a lovely evening, Abey,' she said in the shadows of the porch, looking up at me from within the folds of her huge scarf.

I dared to kiss her and then she disappeared behind the heavy panelled door, leaving me staring at the huge brass door knocker for a full minute after it closed, while reality tried to adjust itself around me. I turned slowly towards the dark shape of the car waiting below and climbed in beside Jenson, apologising for keeping him waiting in the cold.

'You were not as long as I expected, Sir,' he answered, staring into the road ahead where the beams of the headlamps met.

*   *   *

I sat in bed with my chin resting on my knees, staring into the darkness. The vivid sensation of Laura being Marie for those moments had disturbed me and although tired, my mind insisted on going over again what might have happened if I had returned that evening to the old French workshop and Marie.

After a disturbed night I awoke at seven o'clock and again lay thinking over the happenings of past and present. At eight o'clock I washed, shaved, dressed and went into the hall. Mrs Rawlinson came out from what I supposed was the kitchen and led me into the dining-room. She asked if the dance had been successful and I assured her it had been, from my point of view.

As I started on my second lot of toast and marmalade I heard Gerald's voice in the kitchen.

'I've come to return a key,' he said.

'—Anyone up yet?'

'Just Mr Staughton,' Mrs Rawlinson replied.

Gerald came through to the dining-room.

'Hello, Abey!—You're up in good time. Good do last night!—I haven't had breakfast yet.'

Mrs Rawlinson overheard him. 'Would you like some now, Mr Blencoe?'

'Ah now, Mrs Rawlinson, that would be most acceptable!' He sat down next to me. '—What was that last night about you and The Central School?' he asked.

I explained again.

'So you are actually working on a dresser and a bureau at the moment?'

I nodded.

Mrs Rawlinson appeared with two grilled kippers and warned him of the very hot plate they were on.

'I say, that was a splendid band last night, wasn't it?' he said, buttering a slice of bread. As he set about removing one of the kipper backbones he went on 'Look here, why don't I take you out to see that extension we're doing near Oxford? You might have some ideas about the furniture.'

'I'm just going home,' I said, wondering if he was serious.

'It could be an opportunity for you, old son!' he said, attacking the kippers with knife and fork.

'True,' I said.

'Have you made any other arrangements?' he asked.

'No, I haven't.'

He leaned back in his chair.

'The sun's in the sky, the bird's on the wing,
God's in his heaven, All's right with the
    world!'

he misquoted. '—You could come, could you not?'

'I suppose so,' I said buttering yet more toast and wondering what Mrs Pickvance might say if I was very late getting back.

'Fine, that's settled then,' said Gerald. '—Wait a minute though. I've just remembered I promised Mabel to go to Morning Service this morning with her.' He took out a pocket watch and regarded it thoughtfully. 'Nine-twenty. Right, I'll pick you up at say, two o'clock.' He turned and called towards the kitchen 'Will lunch be finished by two, Mrs R?'

'No telling, Sir; everyone's late today,' came back the answer.

At that moment Charlotte appeared. 'What a lot of noise you are making, Gerald! Good morning, Abey. Did you manage to sleep?'

I assured her that I had.

'Just trying to see what time lunch might finish, old thing,' said Gerald. 'I'm going to pick Abey up and take him to see our Oxford job after I've been to church with Mabel.'

'Why don't you bring Mabel round for luncheon and then you and Abey can go off while Mabel and I talk?'

'Thank you!—See you after church then.' He gave Mrs Rawlinson a quick hug saying 'Thanks for the breakfast. You're my favourite kipper cooker!'

The housekeeper blushed slightly, muttering 'Oh, Mr Blencoe, whatever next!'—but Gerald had gone.

Charlotte went to get dressed while outside Gerald's car went off like a rocket.

'That poor Mr Blencoe,' said Mrs Rawlinson; 'all three brothers killed in the war and his mother died not long after he came home. Such a lovely man, too!'

I attended St John's Church with Charlotte where we met some of the friends from the concert. After the service, as we walked past the war memorial, Charlotte became very quiet. She stopped and stood still. I stood with her. After a few moments she turned and went on. I noticed how very well she had mastered the use of her artificial foot.

'It's five years tomorrow since Arthur Pearson Grantle was killed. Nobody else knows, Abey, but I was secretly engaged to him. We were going to announce it when he came back but—he didn't.'

After a little while she went on 'His sister's there now, you know. He fell out with his father and the farm belonged to his mother. It's all so different from what we'd hoped.' After another pause she said 'I've not told anyone else.'

As we turned from Lewisham Way into Wickham Road Charlotte asked 'Isn't it tomorrow you go to college?'

'Yes,' I said.

'Well, if you're staying to lunch now you may as well stay tonight in that room and save yourself a train fare.'

I hesitated, as I was always apprehensive about the possibility of a noisy nightmare and after the recent experience on the dance floor I was even more so. Charlotte would understand this, I thought, so I told her, smiling to hide my embarrassment 'I still get nightmares sometimes and make a lot of noise.'

'Mabel may stay the night but her room and mine are too far away for us to be disturbed and Mrs Rawlinson is slightly deaf,' she answered in a matter-of-fact way. 'And in any case we would all understand—and you managed all right last night.'

'Mrs Pickvance will worry.'

'I'll send her a telegram while you are at Oxford.'

The ride to Oxford was exciting. Gerald drove an open MG Midget two-seater, fast all the way.

'You met old Hartley Trott, then. I was on

270

his staff soon after his Orderly Room in an old school was blown to pieces. Direct hit. I was on a spot of leave in Paris. How did you come across him?'

'I only met him once. Just before that happened. He put me on a job, but I didn't see him again.'

The wind swept through our hair but Gerald had supplied me with goggles and a heavy leather coat to keep me warm. We roared through village and town as flies splattered on the windscreen and folk stood back, some shaking their fists at us.

The house we had come to see was charmingly set just outside a stone-walled Oxfordshire village with dairy shorthorns grazing peacefully in a field at the front. Gerald had brought drawings showing the proposed new wing and, outside the house, explained the details to me. The butler invited us in, suggesting we left again before guests arrived, who were expected later in the afternoon.

The furniture was mostly Elizabethan, heavy oak, beautifully kept and impressive.

'The Blachfords are keen to preserve the style of the building, as you can see from the drawings, but wanted it to reflect something of our own times. Furniture the same. What do you think?'

We talked about new developments in furniture and I described the dresser and bureau I was making which were both in oak. I felt he was slightly wary at the mention of The Arts and Crafts Movement but he listened while I explained some of Mr Spooner's principles and the ideas being worked out at The Central School.

'If you've got time, do a few sketches, Abey. Let me see them. No hurry. The building won't start for another month.'

He took me back to Charlotte's house and we exchanged addresses. He told me he had got a copy of Lethaby's *Form in Civilization* but had never read it. He thought he might try it again now. Mabel came out and put on a driving helmet, they fixed their goggles, bade farewell and departed.

I passed the night with no nightmare but awoke more than once very much aware of my vivid confusion between Marie and Laura. So much so that next day, after a hard day's work at the school, in order to avoid seeing Laura, I did not use the canteen in the evening.

CHAPTER TWENTY-ONE

Tuesday morning seemed about as far from what had happened during the previous three days as was possible. As soon as I arrived at the workshop Mr Hardwick said he wanted to have a word with me. Bertie was anxious to show me the lime he had prepared for the WI shield. At that time of the year in the morning it was always best to get on with something physical in order to keep warm. I stood in the office, my hands thrust deeply into my pockets while Albert looked for a piece of paper on which he had made a few notes. He found it eventually, then after removing his hat, knocked the dust out from it and replaced it. I could see he was agitated.

'Now Abey,' he began, 'we're getting all behind and a lot of things seem to be piling up behind you.'

Bart Cross tapped on the door.

'What is it?' called Albert.

'One of the hens is dead. Looks like crop bound,' said Bart.

'All right, I'll come and look at it in a few minutes,' said Albert.

'Did you want them eggs sending round to Arthur Bourton?' asked Bart.

'Leave it till I come out, Bart. I'm busy at the moment.'

'Ah, all right then,' said Bart, closing the door.

'Now Abey, as I was saying, we're getting behind with things. There's this shield, the Luker's dresser, we've just had two waggons come in for urgent repairs and now, yesterday, I had an enquiry from Remsditch Chamber of Commerce to see if we would like to send in a design for some furniture for their new committee rooms. Mr Luker has led them to believe we would tender for the work.'

This greatly interested me and I asked how long we had got to do it.

'I haven't said we would do it,' said Albert, frowning. 'With you away so much and other work beginning to come in, I'm not sure it would be wise to even consider such a project.'

'I shall be working all next Saturday,' I said, 'and they will only want the drawing and the price at this stage. We might not get the job but it would be good to try for it.'

Albert was quiet for a moment, then 'How much longer will you be going up to London?' he asked.

'Well, it depends on how I get on,' I said, aware that he was waiting for me to finish there but hoping myself to continue for some time yet. I decided to jump in. 'What are the prospects for making this furniture if we get the job?'

'Look Abey, for us to get that job it means you making a drawing, you and me working out a price and then, if we've not been wasting all that time and get the job—a big table and twelve chairs—who is going to make it? Horace was the only man here who ever made a chair of any sort. It will take too long for you to do on your own. I can't afford to hold up the waggon and farm work. Like I've said, it might put customers off to see stuff like that done while they are waiting for carts and

274

things to get on with their seasonal work.'

'Why not let me have Bertie and one other man, say Simon, and see how we get on?—As you say, we might not get the job but it might be good for the workshop if you did get it. They will write about it in the *Remsditch Advertiser*.'

Albert nodded thoughtfully.

'I can get on with the shield today.—Have you priced it yet?—I told Mrs Maycock you would let her know.'

Albert nodded again, then said 'Difficult, that is. Mrs Hardwick is on the WI committee and says I should not charge for it, it being for the good of the community.'

'Mrs Maycock hinted at that,' I said, then, returning to the previous discussion, 'When has the design got to be in for that furniture?'

'About a month from now,' said Albert, 'but it could come up just when the seasonal work is at its thickest and we could lose business through it.'

'If I got the Luker dresser done we could perhaps let the committee see it,' I suggested.

Albert liked that idea. 'Ah well, you'll have to do the drawing in the evenings. You better go and get on now. See how far George and Harry are with those two waggons and when they are done you best get that shield done. Use Bertie as much as you can.'

'If I worked an extra hour from six till seven in the week would you make up some of the pay I don't get on Mondays?' I asked him.

'I might,' he said.

'If I can persuade Bertie to stay sometimes it would help us to catch up and I might get the Luker dresser done sooner,' I said, following Albert out into the yard where Bart was waiting for him.

'They're in the shed there,' said Bart.

Albert picked up one of the ailing hens.

'Crop bound. Get that needle and thread from the shelf in the office, Abey.'

I went to find it.

When I returned Albert was holding one of the sickly hens firmly under his arm, its head in one hand and a sharp penknife in the other. He slit along the side of its crop where it was impacted with corn. Then, opening the cut, he poked out the corn and quickly sewed the skin together with the needle and thread, using big stitches. He tied the ends of the thread and set the hen down on the ground, where it staggered slightly for a moment then ran to join the others. He picked up the second hen and as I walked back to the workshop I heard him tell Bart that he must make sure that the hens could find their flint grit for digestion as well as the limestone grit for making eggshells.

I found Bertie by the circular-saw bench mending a puncture in his bicycle.

'Come on, you can't do that now,' I said. 'There's work to be done on those two waggons.'

276

'How shall I get home?'

'You'll have to do that after work or at dinner time.'

'I thought we was goin' to do that shield and then the dresser,' said Bertie.

'They're waiting for the waggons.'

'There's always somebody waiting for something!'

'And a good thing, too! There's many a person without a job today. Think yourself fortunate,' I said.

'I was told I would be making a toolbox for myself when I came here!' complained Bertie as we headed for the shop.

'So you will, when there's a minute for you to do it.'

'And a bowsaw,' he added.

'I'm going to be working till seven each night for a while. Are you prepared to join me?' I asked him.

'What! An extra hour, every night?'

I nodded.

'What for?'

'To catch up, and get on with that furniture.'

'Well, I don't know,' he said reluctantly. 'I shall have to ask my mum.'

George and Harry were looking at one of the waggons. Part of the frame called the turning circle had distorted so that it would not turn. One of the bearers had partly rotted and was allowing the frame to bind against the main frame.

'Have to come right out,' said Harry.

George agreed. 'Best get 'er jacked up,' he said.

'What's the trouble with the other one?' I asked.

'Only a broken shaft. If you see to that one, Abey, we'll get this one apart, then when you've done we shall need a hand here. They're waitin' for both of 'em up at Crosswood.'

Bertie and I went to sort out a piece of suitable timber. Carefully selected ash with the grain running straight through or slightly curved to follow the shape of a waggon shaft was kept set aside for this purpose. The long grain of the ash planed beautifully and I stood for a few moments watching as Bertie walked backwards and forwards, pushing his long try-plane from one end to the other of the piece we had selected, each time sending a tightly curled, wiry shaving whistling out through the mouth of his plane.

*　　　*　　　*

By the end of the month the WI shield was fixed in the village hall, I had discussed with Mr Spooner the design for the Chamber of Commerce furniture, prepared a drawing and sent it for their consideration, finished the carcase of the dresser and was working with Bertie on the drawers in the evening. Mr

Spooner, I discovered, was also involved with a workshop of his own, and from time to time I went to see exhibitions of his furniture during my days in London.

About this time I visited an exhibition in London of handmade furniture designed by the famous Gordon Russell, who later went on to successfully adapt his designs to machine making.

CHAPTER TWENTY-TWO

Mr Spooner realised when I first began in London that my experience had not included the making of fine dovetails, but with the practice that he insisted upon I learned to mark out and make examples of the common through-dovetail, the lap dovetail, as used in drawer construction, and also the secret mitre dovetail. Being well practised with the hand tools, I was able to produce a reasonable result and then after further practice I was able to use this construction in my furniture making. I was sorry old Horace was not able to see my efforts but young Bertie was quick to pick up the idea and set about making a dovetailed tool-box for himself.

One evening we were clearing up when Greg Mottram looked in at the workshop. 'Ah Abey, tell old Albert that we're ready for that show-chest he said he'd do for us. It's to put the stuff in to take to the horse shows.' Seeing Bertie's box in the making, he exclaimed 'Why, there it is! He's got it under way already. Good old Albert! Tell him the first show is in two weeks. It'll need two good strong handles and a good lock with two keys.—You've never been up to see the horses, Abey. Come up one evening. We've got some beauties there now. The missus was pleased with that little dogcart you did for her. You made a good job of that!'

As he swept round the benches he did not seem to notice Bertie scowling, just waiting for him to leave so that he could express his opinion of him.

'What cheek!' he exclaimed as soon as the door closed. 'Doesn't it occur to him that there might be someone else in the world needing a box.—He'll be lucky to get one in a fortnight!'

Another evening Mr Luker came in to see how the dresser was progressing and told me that my drawings for the proposed Chamber of Commerce were attracting a lot of interest.

*   *   *

One Monday towards Easter I came out of the furniture school workshop and found Laura waiting in the corridor. I was completely unprepared for this and must have looked very surprised.

She smiled apprehensively. 'Oh, hello Abey.

Can I have a word with you?'

We moved over to the side of the corridor to allow others to pass.

'Yes, of course.'

She looked straight at me as she asked 'Why have you been avoiding me?'

I did not know what to say. Not able to just stand there looking at each other, we edged along in the stream of students until we reached the main doors. It was still light outside and the traffic was moving fast along Southampton Row.

'I'll get my coat,' said Laura.

I looked at her, struck dumb for a moment, then asked 'Where are you going?'

'I thought we might walk along outside.'

'Oh, er, yes,' I murmured.

'It's quite cold. Have you got a coat?'

'I'll get it.'

Outside we walked towards Holborn underground station. Amidst the rumble and clatter of horse and carriage, tram and motor omnibus, newsboys were shouting about a coal strike. Neither of us spoke until we came to a small café.

Laura suggested some coffee. The aroma of the steaming coffee and sitting close to Laura immediately brought back my memory of Marie with her strong black coffee and thick white mugs.

I nervously shot a glance at Laura who caught my eye and smiled reassuringly. 'I shouldn't have brought you out like this. I didn't mean to embarrass you.'

'I'm not embarrassed,' I said. 'I've wanted to see you all the time, but . . .'

'What's wrong then?' she asked.

I stirred the milk into my coffee and stared into the swirling liquid.

'Fear, I suppose.'

'Fear! What d'you mean?'

There was a long pause and we both drank well down into our cups before I spoke again, still staring into my cup.

'When I was in France I met a girl called Marie . . . She was young and very beautiful. I fell in love with her. She completely entranced me. I was on a short leave pass. She lived on the outskirts of a small town with her stepfather, a wheelwright. I was due to go back to camp with a friend that night. I told her I would find him to say I wasn't going back to the army and that I'd return to her. She smiled and shook her head and told me I wouldn't come back. When I found my friend in the town he arranged with some other soldier friends to take me back to camp against my will, knowing the penalty for desertion.— Within a few weeks the war ended and I went to find her.'

I paused again and glanced at Laura. She was holding her cup with both hands, leaning forward and listening with big round eyes.

'The place was deserted. I enquired from

neighbours. She had run off with an English soldier, a deserter, to Paris. The army redcaps traced him. He shot her and himself.' I went on staring into my coffee cup. I did not look at Laura.

'Oh, Abey!' she said quietly.

'More coffee, Sir?' asked the waiter, taking our empty cups onto his tray.

'Er, well, yes. More coffee, please,' I said, looking up at Laura. Her eyes were moist as she nodded to the waiter.

When the coffee arrived and we had stirred in our milk, I began again. 'When I danced the last waltz with you that night I suddenly had a strange sensation that I was dancing with Marie. I hadn't been thinking about her at all, and it was unnerving.—I slept badly that night—and I'm afraid my war memories may haunt me for ever. I tend to avoid situations where there may be a risk of arousing them.'

'Oh Abey, I don't know what to say. I'm so sorry,' Laura said, leaning forward to squeeze my hand. I felt suddenly embarrassed and looked round at other people in the café.

I attempted to lighten what I had just related by going on: 'My landlady keeps a bucket of cold water outside my bedroom door to deal with my nightmares!'

Laura smiled. 'I shouldn't have sought you out like this. It just seemed so strange that I never saw you again after such a lovely evening.'

'It was wrong of me to avoid you. I did it at first because it was easier and then, well, it became more difficult to meet you again. I'm sorry, and thank you for hoicking me out of my "slough of despond".'

She smiled. 'We'll be late for the classes!'

I paid for the coffee and we ran, holding hands, back along Southampton Row.

When nearly at the school I said 'Why don't we go to the cinema instead?'

We stopped, looked at each other and laughed.

'Why not!' she cried.

We hugged each other for a moment under the street lights and then as the traffic idled or twinkled past we turned and ran back to the underground station.

*   *   *

Over the Easter break I did not see Laura again but we started writing to each other. I finished the dresser for Mr Luker and he was generous in his praise of the 'craftsmanship in its making' and 'bringing out the great beauty of the oak'. I believe he showed it to friends of his who were influential in the Chamber of Commerce; at any rate, shortly afterwards we received the commission to make the furniture for their new committee rooms. Albert was pleased with the result but concerned about how the work would be carried out, because preparation for the summer work was already beginning on the farms.

While Laura and I sat with Jimmy Townsend one Monday evening in the art school canteen I mentioned the problem to him.

'Would you consider helping if I could find someone to put you up and get Albert to pay you?'

'I might do that.—Why not?' he said. 'I could come as soon as term ends here.'

Albert looked doubtful when I mentioned it. 'I don't know, Abey. You're all the while putting pressure on me and I can't afford to pay an extra man just now.'

'But it will bring in more profit,' I argued, 'and get things moving more quickly.'

'Ah, so it might, but the shop will get too full. The men won't like it.'

'We could use the straw barn if it gets too tight in the shop. You won't need that again until harvest and it's nearly empty now. If Jimmy Townsend comes and I have Jes or Simon and Bertie we should get it done quite quickly,' I said.

'Ah well, I suppose we shall have to do it somehow,' concluded Albert. But he still looked worried.

'Oh, Mr Staughton, would you give me an 'and in 'ere a moment?'

Nellie Hawtin had come out of the cowshed. A first calf heifer was standing with one back foot firmly in a pail of milk and would not be pushed off it. I spoke quietly to her and she eyed me nervously. I could feel her trembling slightly when I placed my hand on her. I waited, still talking quietly for a few moments, then I began to push her sideways so that she would have to move her back legs to keep her balance. The bucket scraped noisily then, BANG! The pail and I were against the wall and the white liquid, already discoloured by the heifer's foot, splattered and ran down the wall behind and into the dung channel.

'Well I never!' said Nellie. 'Just you fancy 'er doin' that! Thank you, Mr Staughton, I'll clear all that up. I expect you're busy in there. Remind Mrs Pickvance it's our turn to clean the church this Saturday; and by the way, you'll be pleased to know my sister's made a full recovery.'

*　　　*　　　*

The design for the Chamber of Commerce furniture, much influenced by my studies of the Arts and Crafts leaders of the time, was very simple. The only decoration was done with stopped chamfering, which can be very effective and is much used by the wheelwright because it reduces weight without diminishing strength. The teaching of Charles Spooner at The Central School, backed by the influence of men like Gimson, the Barnsleys and now the encouragement of Gordon Russell and Ambrose Heal, had awakened in me a delight in the spirit of the native English style that was associated with the oak and walnut styles of the seventeenth century.

To find suitable oak for the table top was not easy: two and a half inches thick to allow for levelling, cut on the radius to reveal the beautiful medullary-ray figuring, in fairly wide boards twelve foot long without a serious blemish; it required a lot of finding and turning over of timber. Stuff to make six legs, rails for tenoning to the legs and the pieces for the top were selected and then work began on the heavy planing, out in the old straw barn where we had put our benches. It attracted attention from all round once it began to take shape. I set Bertie and Simon to prepare timber for the chairs while Jimmy and myself finished scraping the table top, ready for fuming the oak with ammonia when it was finished, to get a lovely dark mellow colour before the final polishing with beeswax.

One day I had an unexpected visit from Gerald, who came into the workshop to find me when he was on the way to see an architectural client. I had gone up to Lonestock with Bertie to sort out a waggon with a broken wheel. We had taken Magnolia and were removing the wheel in the farm rickyard when Gerald appeared.

'Not an easy chap to find!' he exclaimed

clasping my hand. 'Thought I'd find you chopping out a chair or turning out a table!'

'So you might have done if you'd come at a different time,' I said. 'We're just getting this wheel off and going back to the shop. If you're not in a hurry I can show you some furniture we're doing.'

'Always in a hurry, old chap. Can't stay long. Wondered if you'd had any thoughts about that furniture for Oxford?'

'I haven't had a chance, really,' I said. 'Work is pretty demanding at the moment.'

Gerald helped us load the wheel onto our cart and we pulled out onto the road where Gerald had left his MG.

Bertie's eyes were wide with admiration when he saw it.

'Can't wait while you drive that thing down to the village,' said Gerald, nodding towards Magnolia.

I set Bertie to bring the cart down and told him I would go with Gerald.

'Some folks!' Bertie spluttered, and we swept off, leaving him open-mouthed.

I could tell Gerald liked the table and the chairs, too, as far as we had got with them.

'Do me some sketches. Suggestions. You won't necessarily have to make it all,' he said and I agreed to try. 'I'll come and take you over there again. Let me see this stuff when you've finished it.' He was off again before Bertie arrived back with Magnolia.

I had noticed lately that Magnolia was slower than she used to be and this morning I thought she stumbled once on the way up to the farm. I mentioned it to Albert.

'Ah, I've noticed it myself. She's getting on, of course, like all of us. Bart says she's eating all right and she still keeps Jiffy in her place. I've been keeping an eye on her.'

'That car!' said Bertie when we were back at the bench. '—What does he do for a living?'

'Architect,' I said.

'What are we doing messing about with wooden wheels!' he exclaimed with some feeling.

'A car like that wouldn't be a lot of use on a farm,' I pointed out.

'Maybe not. But with a car like that who would want to be on a farm?' said Bertie, releasing some pent up feeling in the production of the next few shavings from his plane.

*　　　*　　　*

Jimmy Townsend had stayed at the vicarage for the few weeks he was involved with the furniture making and was due to return to London soon. I had discussed the sketches for Gerald with him and he thought it a very good idea to be following it up.

'Sort of thing that could lead to good work,' he said. 'Pity you couldn't spend a bit more time up with Spooner.'

I thought this, too, but knew it was out of the question as even the time I did spend there was always under threat.

Soon after Jimmy had gone back Albert called me into his office. 'Abey, I'm going to look at a horse over at Sendersby. He's eight years old and worked on the farm up there. Greg Mottram says he'll go up and look at him if I thought seriously about having him. Magnolia's not what she used to be for the heavier work and this might be an opportunity. I thought you and I could go up and look at him this afternoon.'

To save a bit of time we took our dinner bags with us and set off with Jiffy in the dogcart. We commented on the various stages of farming around us as we sped along the bumpy road. The old gate that Pip had thrown open when we had once driven Magnolia in to contend with Archie Bowler's bull was still there, and then I thought of Roderick Walker driving me back from Remsditch in his cart just before he had enlisted in the army. All that remained of both of them was their names carved into the memorial stone in the church wall.

'Over in that field on the hill there,' said the farmer when Albert enquired about the horse. 'Follow the path to the gate. You'll see him. He's in there with some sheep. You can go in. He's very good natured.'

The lane we walked along was strewn with poppies and clover. We stood and leaned on the gate to look at the chestnut-coloured horse with a white blaze on his nose, slightly smaller than Magnolia but quite powerful looking. We went across to him and he went on grazing while we walked round him. We agreed he looked all right and that Greg Mottram should look at him for us.

On the way home Albert unexpectedly pulled up at a roadside inn. 'We missed our dinnertime drink so we'll make up for it here,' he said as I followed him inside.

When we were settled at a table with a glass of ale apiece he said 'I've brought you in here, Abey, to tell you that things are going to be different soon. I've been seeing Doctor Savings on and off lately and he says that I've got to take things easier. You know how difficult that is at the shop and I'm considering selling the business.'

I was astonished. It had never crossed my mind that such a thing could be in the offing.

'I've not told anyone yet but I wanted you to know in case you might be interested in taking it on.'

'How could I?' I said, slightly stunned by the news. 'I've got no capital.'

'I wondered if your father might help you and you could perhaps get a loan. The business is good now and with the extra work you're doing it could develop even more.'

'It's a bit of a shock,' I said, 'coming out of the blue like that. What sort of price is involved?'

'Ah well, I don't know yet. Now I've spoken to you I shall get a valuation on it and it will give you a chance to find out what's possible. Best not to say anything at this stage as the men will get unsettled about their jobs.'

I agreed to give it some thought, even though I was far from confident about the outcome. 'When's all this likely to take place?' I asked.

'Within the next six months,' answered Albert.

*   *   *

I gave Albert's proposition a great deal of thought. At first I considered it to be out of the question but then I began to think that such an opportunity might not come again and would be even less likely to do so if I waited until all the conditions were set fair.

There were two overriding requirements: money and ability. Money was measurable and it was possible to calculate whether enough was available. Ability was only assessable through one's own eyes and feelings. To do the practicalities of the trade and craft was not the same as being able to run it as a successful business, inspiring customers and making enough profit to pay men's wages as well as maintain the establishment.

I went to talk it over with my father and brothers. It would be difficult to raise money from the farm without taking capital, especially as farming was depressed at the time. Father offered to make over to me a hundred pounds if it would help and said he would try to secure a loan if necessary. There was no house with the property and I would need to consider something one day, when Mrs Pickvance's house was no longer available to me.

Within a few more weeks the village found out about Albert's intending retirement and buzzed with speculation. The men were apprehensive and talked constantly about the future, even though Albert assured them he would only hand the business over to someone who would accept responsibility for their jobs. Everyone knew this was impossible to guarantee and consequently remained apprehensive.

I made time to see Laura every Monday. She came from work on Mondays to have lunch with me at the little café in Southampton Row and between classes in the evenings we again went out for walks or visited exhibitions together. She came to stay at Mrs Pickvance's one weekend and set the village alight with speculation. I went to stay with her another weekend and met her family. I talked to her about all the problems and possibilities of the

293

wheelwright and carpentry business and also the growing success of the furniture work, for now Gerald's firm of architects had commissioned a number of items for the Oxford house and Mr Luker was considering designs for a dining table.

One Monday just before the summer recess Laura brought me a note from Charlotte asking if I could meet her the following Monday. At the school the following week there was to be an exhibition of students' work including my bureau as well as a chair and a turned lampstand I had made, so at once I wrote a note back inviting her and suggesting she met me there during the morning.

With all the work that was going on at home in the workshop I had considered missing out the London trip that particular week, but knowing I should not be seeing Laura for some time and now having had Charlotte's note, I easily, although somewhat guiltily, caught the train to town on the morning of the exhibition's opening.

Charlotte enjoyed seeing the great range of art and craftwork produced by the school. Pottery, weaving, lettering and calligraphy, embroidery, furniture making, ironwork, copper and silversmithing, drawing and painting, printing, screenprinting and dressmaking were all represented.

Afterwards we went out to the café where she wanted to talk privately to me.

'Now Abey, I understand that the wheel-wright's business at home is up for sale?'

'Yes,' I said. 'How did you hear that?'

'I hear all the local news from Mother. Most of it doesn't interest me particularly but this did.—How much are they asking for it?'

I was surprised at the question. 'Why, twelve hundred pounds, I believe—lock, stock and barrel,' I said.

'Are you going to buy it?' she asked.

'Me?'

'You will, won't you?'

'What with?'

'How much have you got?'

I shrugged. 'Nothing, really. I could probably raise a hundred or two, including borrowing.'

'You'll need that for working capital. I'll buy it and you can rent it from me.'

'What!'

'*I'll* buy it and *you* can rent it from me,' she repeated. 'I need to put some money into something and I know you'll do all right. I didn't want to interfere if you were going to buy it, but now I'll get my solicitor to make the offer.'

'Are you sure you want to do this?' I asked in amazement.

'Absolutely. I'm still attached to the old village, even though it has no use for me. This will give me a connection with it and keep me in touch with you.'

I thanked her, adding 'If it all comes off I'll look forward to being your tenant.'

Later I told Laura what had been said.

'How marvellous, Abey! I'm so pleased and excited for you.—I expect it will mean the end of your visits here to The Central School but it will be a wonderful opportunity.'

When I said goodbye to Laura that night after the classes I asked her a question. 'If it does all work out and I get the place, will you marry me and help make it work?'

'Oh Abey, I'd love to! Of course I will! Oh Abey, yes!'

I missed the next train home while we talked about where we might live in the village and how soon the wedding might be arranged, after I had been to see her parents again to ask permission from her father.

I seemed to pedal my bicycle faster every time I came back on the train from London but this time I surely broke all records.

CHAPTER TWENTY-THREE

Greg Mottram went to look at the new horse and gave a favourable report. The deal was done and Jes went over with Albert to bring Strongbow back. Magnolia did not welcome him. Jiffy ran to the far end of the field but Magnolia stood so close to the gate that it was impossible to get him inside without Jes putting a halter on her and leading her away while Albert opened the gate. As soon as she was released she moved behind the newcomer with the idea of biting his behind and chasing him. He gave way for a little while, until he had sized up the situation then, unlike Jiffy, he suddenly stopped running and turned to face the established matron. She swerved round him to attack his rear but at the crucial moment he turned and let fly with his back legs, catching her a hefty thump from his iron shoes on her shoulder. This dissuaded her somewhat and she gave up the attack. He went over and sniffed around Jiffy, who eyed him nervously, but nothing happened and the three of them, with Magnolia and Jiffy standing very close together and the new gentleman just a little way off, quietened down.

'That was a nasty thump he gave poor old Magnolia!' said Albert. 'She's not really up to that sort of treatment. She's gone very quiet. She'll have a bruise there and a stiff shoulder. I'll get Bart to put some liniment on it before nightfall.'

I realised it might be up to me to make the decision about Magnolia's future, but this was only one of a number of new decisions I would have to be making soon.

The village and the workshop in particular were buzzing with the news of me taking over the workshop. Fortunately I got great support from the men in the shop, although one or two expressed some concern about the furniture making in relation to the local needs of wheelwrighting and carpentry.

Mrs Pickvance was overjoyed at the news and when I told her I was getting married, bless her, she threw her arms round me and cried with delight. 'That lovely girl! You lucky boy!' she shouted. 'Where will you live then?—You can come here with her if you like, but you'll be wanting your own place now you're takin' over from Albert!'

At church I was greeted by everyone when I came down from ringing the bell and Maisie Hawtin and Jenny were among the first to congratulate me.

'I'll even forgive you for not coming to the concert now!' laughed Jenny.

*   *   *

That Sunday evening as the sun went down behind the blacksmith's house and yard, I stood in front of the war memorial and read its names once more, wondering why it was me who had been spared to stand there noticing the tiny lichen forming in the serifs of the Roman Lettered inscription, while I felt the utter finality of the lot of those who would 'grow not old as we that are left grow old'. As I turned away in the silence of the closing day I remembered the time when I had longed, with

298

them, to be back here with its folk in this old village. But the simple innocence of the life they remembered was never the same again, for those days with their threads of innocent laughter and sunshine, of which those young men had been a part, had gone with them for ever.